Photography by Peter Barry
Designed by Philip Clucas
Produced by Ted Smart and David Gibbon

Hair artists: Pat Spires, and Trevor Walker of
    Sizzerin Hot, East Twickenham,
Middlesex.
Make-up: Kim Walker.
Hair care products: Wella Great Britain.
Baby Care products: Boots Ltd.
Wigs and electrical equipment: The House
    of Carmen.
Hair ornaments: Madesils, London.
Morris Masterclass International, London.
Clothes design: Kate Anthony – long, white
    silk jacket; Penny Warner – black jacket
    with check collar; Sarah Windsor – blue
    and white spotted sweater; Fred Spur of
    Whispers in the Ear – white crushed silk
    top with collar; No? Yes! – premier coat
    in pink.

CLB 1567
Published in Great Britain 1986 by Colour Library
    Books Ltd., Guildford, Surrey, England.
© 1986 Illustrations: Colour Library Books Ltd.,
    and Wella Great Britain.
© 1986 Text: Colour Library Books Ltd.
Printed and bound in Barcelona, Spain.
All rights reserved.
ISBN 0 86283 414 7
Leg. B-27.772-85

HAIR CARE

Pat Spires

COLOUR LIBRARY BOOK

Contents

Introduction

Healthy, shiny hair looks so good whether it's cut short and sassy or left long and flowing. Hair styles today range from the outrageous to the classically elegant; literally anything goes as long as it complements the wearer, fits in with her lifestyle and reflects her personality.

With the modern styling techniques and products that are available today, women can become as adaptable as the chameleon, changing looks at will (whatever the length of their hair) to suit different moods, clothes and occasions.

Beautiful hair is the body's greatest natural fashion accessory. It can be curled or coaxed into the most incredible shapes to enhance your appearance and complement your clothes. Few fashion accessories are as pliable or as versatile and yet how many of us really appreciate it?

Well here is the opportunity to show your hair a little care and consideration. All it takes is just these ten easy steps and you are on your way to beautiful hair.

Step **1.** A healthy, balanced diet. For super hair and a clear skin.

Step **2.** Stimulate that circulation. After all it's the blood that supplies your hair with nourishment.

Step **3.** Learn to relax. You're more likely to keep your hair if you do.

Step **4.** Cleanliness. This means hair, brushes, combs and rollers too.

Step **5.** Condition. A must after every shampoo.

Versatile styles are the order of the day. Right: hair in poor condition, unevenly coloured and out of shape will not respond well or look attractive when styled. But when those faults have been corrected a new woman emerges.
Subtle, temporary changes in shade can be achieved with coloured mousse, while a simple, long, layered cut is extremely adaptable and can be worn straight, gently waved or curly.

Step **6.** The cut. A good cut is an investment and the foundation for any hairstyling service.

Step **7.** Products. Choose with care, seek professional advice or select well-known brand names.

Step **8.** Styling Equipment. The right tools for the job makes all the difference.

Step **9.** Curls. Perms and relaxers require special care: you'll need to adjust your conditioning routine for these.

Step **10.** Colour. Make it a colourful year. Whether it's outrageous or very discreet, colour can add new dimensions to your hair.

As you read through the book you will find more and more information relating to these ten easy steps. Quite simply, it's the how, why and when to beautiful hair.

Hair-The Fundamentals

Healthy hair looks and feels so good. To keep it that way it's important to choose and use high quality shampoos and conditioners that will gently cleanse and protect each strand.

What or who do you blame or bless for the texture, condition, colour of your hair: products? the hairdresser? your parents? Natural hair colour and texture tend to be hereditary, as does the colour of our eyes and skin, but condition; now that's a different matter altogether. The condition and appearance of your hair can be greatly enhanced by the way you and your hairdresser treat it. Badly permed, relaxed, tinted or bleached and it will look lifeless, dull or frizzy, and if the worst happens it may split or break off at the scalp. Correctly treated and conditioned and its appearance plus manageability should improve, even though the shine and general condition are purely cosmetic.

Manufacturers have spent thousands of pounds in the last decade or so developing products to colour and curl our hair in the gentlest possible way. A good, modern shampoo no longer strips the hair of all its natural oils, leaving it dry and flyaway, and conditioners have forged ahead, progressing from a purely cosmetic coating of the hair shaft – for smoothness

and shine – to complex restructurants which have a variety of uses. Some are designed to replace moisture and reduce brittleness, others actually penetrate into the hair, where they help temporarily to repair and strengthen the damaged internal structure.

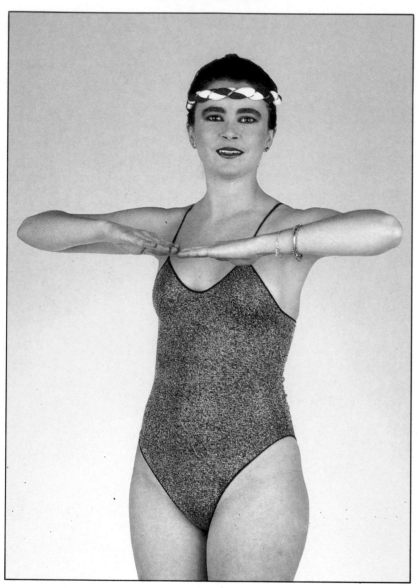

Healthy hair growth depends a great deal on how well our bodies function. Regular exercise helps to keep muscles toned and stimulates the circulation. When combined with a nourishing, well balanced diet your hair and skin can't fail to reap the benefits.

Even so, with all these wonderful products around, the responsibility for the condition of our hair still rests squarely on our own shoulders or, to be more correct, in our mouths. "You are what you eat" could not more aptly describe our hair in relation to our diet. Most of us are b now – thanks to the media – familiar with what constitutes a healthy diet and healthy lifestyle. A balanced diet keeps the body functioning correctly, keeps the skin clear, prevents nails from splitting and helps teeth and gums stay healthy. All these facts are thrust in front of us every day, from early breakfast TV to the last high-fibre cereal advertisement at night. But did you realise that it's equally important for the hair? You only have to think back to your last cold or stomach upset to know how quickly your hair reacts to physical illness. Consequently, the result of a poor diet will soon manifest itself in the state of your hair. No, I am not about to launch the special 'S' Plan Diet that will save your hair and rock the nation: basic dietary common sense is all that's required.

Perhaps you are wondering how what you eat can affect your hair, especially as the hair we see and spend so much time, money and effort on is dead. Yes, I'm afraid that's true: once it appears above the scalp your hair is dead. Hair does not contain any blood vessels or nerve endings, which is why it doesn't bleed or hurt when we cut it.

Hair grows from an indentation or pocket in the skin called the follicle. At the bottom of the follicle is the hair papilla and this is where all the action takes place. The papilla is continually producing cells; these cells are pushed up and out of the follicle and as they move upwards they harden until they emerge as hard keratin, a protein we recognize as hair.

To ensure that the cells continue to reproduce, the papilla has a rich blood supply busily conveying the essential amino acids and nutrients for the hair's production. The papilla also has its own complex system of nerves, hence the reason for pain when your hair is tugged or pulled out.

From this simplified version of hair growth it's easy to deduce that if your blood lacks a reasonable supply of essential amino acids and nutrients then you hair will react, and if your diet is very poor, as with anorexics, excessive hair loss could result.

Stress and tension can also take their toll, so it's a good idea to take up some form of light exercise to help you relax and unwind. Energetic aerobics seems to be going out of favour, but swimming, cycling, walking and badminton are excellent ways to increase your oxygen intake and stimulate the circulation; all of which will benefit your hair.

From the hair inside to the hair outside. Everyone's hair is as individual as a fingerprint, and yet its basic structure is always the same. The outer layer, or cuticle, helps to protect the more complex, delicate cortex. The cuticle resembles the overlapping scales of a fish, and when hair is in good condition these scales lie flat and

act as a mirror, reflecting light that enhances hair colour and gloss. The cortex is more complicated as it's here that the hair's strength, texture and elasticity, as well as the melanin which gives hair its natural colour can be found. The bonds that are affected by any hairstyling process or chemical treatment are found in the cortex: this is why the state of the cuticle is so important, as it acts like a protective overcoat. The medulla runs through the centre of the hair and is not always present, its function is still unknown and whether you have one or not seems to have little affect on hairstyling services.

Cleanliness is the next stage to hair health. Shampooing: to many this is a simple process but it's often carried out incorrectly to the detriment of both hair and scalp.

Top: many would envy Sue's naturally wavy, red hair, and yet hair of this texture and colour has its problems, with a tendency to look dry and dull.
An acid-balanced shampoo will help, but to encourage a more visible sheen we applied a moisturising protein treatment. This counteracts the dryness, strengthens the hair and closes the cuticle.
Bottom: finally a cut – to remove any dry, split ends – and an application of hair mousse to add body, control the curl and enhance the shine.

Choosing a shampoo is the first step, and whenever possible seek your hairdresser's advice as he may retail a line which is eminently suitable for your hair. Without assistance you face the daunting prospect of selecting from row on row of shampoos on display at the chemist's. Before you purchase, assess your hair type: is it dry, greasy or normal? Read labels carefully; for dry hair choose a cream or oil type shampoo, for greasy hair a lemon or liquid type and for normal hair a cream. Check that it's pH balanced – slightly acidic – this makes it more compatible with the hair and scalp, which are also acidic. If you shampoo daily because of your job, sports or overactive oil (sebaceous) glands, or greasy hair, select one of the gentle shampoos recommended for daily use.

To shampoo, assemble towels, brushes, combs, shampoo and shampoo spray. Dilute a good tablespoon of the shampoo you are going to use in warm water; this will prevent you from using excessive amounts and help the shampoo spread more evenly through the hair. Brush your hair thoroughly, removing any tangles or back-combing, wet the hair with warm water, pour the diluted shampoo over it and gently massage the hair and scalp, then rinse thoroughly. Often, it is not necessary to give a second shampoo but if it is then repeat the procedure. If you suffer from a greasy scalp then shampoo with tepid water and massage gently to avoid stimulating the oil-producing glands.

After shampooing, it's time to condition. All hair benefits from a conditioner. The cosmetic types are surface conditioners which will make combing easier because they encourage the cuticle to lie flat, therefore promoting a healthy, shiny look.

As I mentioned previously, restructurants penetrate into the cortex, attaching themselves to the broken or damaged bonds, and basically they help to strengthen the hair. This makes them ideal for those of us who overdo the blow-drying or chemical processes. Made from hydrolised protein, they are able to penetrate because their molecular size and makeup is very similar to that of your hair. Moisturisers and hot oil treatments are great for those with very dry hair and scalp, particularly black hair which tends to be naturally dry and brittle. Today's modern oils are light and penetrating, far better than the thick grease and hair dressings that are still around which clog the pores of the scalp, often giving rise to more serious scalp problems.

With any form of conditioner or treatment, follow the directions. After shampooing, towel blot out the excess water (do not rub), apply the product, massage or comb through with a wide-toothed comb and leave for the specified time, then remove as directed. If your hair is in really poor condition don't expect miracles with just one treatment as it will take a regular course of restructants to improve badly damaged hair, just as it takes a full course of antibiotics to relieve an infection. Once your hair is in reasonable condition you can switch to a maintenance programme. Usually, this will entail a light conditioner after every shampoo with a restructurant treatment once a month.

Finally, lets take a look at hair types, texture and density. Texture refers to the diameter of each individual strand; density to the amount of hair on your head.

Fine hair can be fairly dense but, unfortunately, it is usually thin as well. An additional problem can be that it is often soft and fly-away: this can be controlled with the use of setting lotions, mousses, etc. As a rule this hair type is best kept short and simple. One length bobs to the jaw-line work well if the hair is straight; shorter bobs and layered designs if it's curly or wavy. A soft perm adds body but it must be done carefully to avoid hair breakage.

Inset: dry, naturally curly, almost frizzy hair like Christine's is often thought to be of a coarse, wiry texture when in fact it can be quite the opposite – baby fine.
Facing page: a damson semi-permanent colour puts some 'oomph' back into Christine's hair and improves the general condition. The balanced cut retains the length, but alters the shape of the style, adding width to a rather long face.

Above: what do you do if your hair is very short, straight, coarse and you are impatient for a new look? Answer: try a support perm (above right and facing page), providing, of course, that your hair is long enough to wind around a perm curler. The result: a lovely, soft, gamine look that suits Sue's facial features to a 'T'.

Medium/normal hair can be worn any way depending on what suits the individual. Although this type of hair is good tempered, it may still require a perm when a full or bouncy style is desired. If your hair is naturally curly or wavy make the most of it; have it cut to enhance the natural movement.

Coarse hair feels thick and dense and requires regular cutting. Although initially more difficult to style, the results can be superb. Short or long will depend on your physical characteristics. Sharp geometrics look stunning on straight hair, whilst wavy or curly hair can be worn in short or very long layers. This type of hair responds well to perming and colouring.

Knowing your hair and how it grows will help you to make the most of your crowning glory besides giving you a better understanding of the problems your hairdresser has to cope with. Manufacturers and hairdressers would love to work miracles, but the hair type sets its own limitations. If you know your hair you will appreciate what will and will not work. It won't stop you yearning for long, blonde, straight hair when yours is red and curly, but it will help.

CHAPTER 2

From Babe to Junior Miss

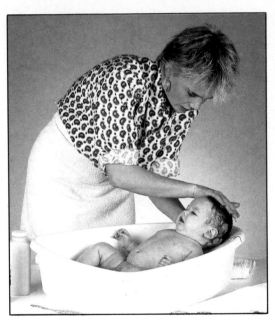

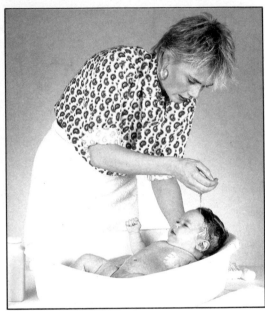

Never pour neat shampoo straight onto the baby's head, spread it onto your hands first, then transfer to the hair. Rinse very thoroughly, remembering to support the baby's head throughout.

Facing page: clean from head to toe; just the finishing touches to Jemma's coiffure with a soft, baby brush. Mind you, at this age, obviously a thumb is far more interesting.

From a babe in arms to the ages of five or six are the years when you can expect your preferences about your child's hairstyle to be adhered to, but from then on you can expect it to be an uphill struggle. It is surprising how aware very young children become of hairstyles and clothes, and this can be for a variety of reasons. One of the most common of these occurs when the child starts playing with other children or going to play-school, where she will come into contact with lots of little girls. Suddenly she has lots of best friends and really wants to "have a slide like Claire" or "long hair like Diana". Fashion is not so important as a desire to be like one of her friends. This is where it can get tricky, but let's go back to that calm before the storm when she is still a little baby and your decision is final.

The amount of hair we have, its type and texture, is decided before we are born (see chapter on "Your Hair During Pregnancy"). At birth the baby's head may be covered with a fine, downy hair – lanugo – or she may be completely bald. Normally, any fine hair will disappear over the next few weeks, and the hair colour and texture at birth, therefore, cannot be taken as a clear indication of the child's eventual hair type.

Children are not all programmed to start growing hair at the same age, and those with fair hair may appear to have far less than their dark-haired playmates purely because the hair tends to be finer and the fairness creates an optical illusion of less hair. Personally, I can well remember photographs of myself which at a quick glance make me look almost bald, but on closer inspection the odd whitish curly tendril can be seen. So don't panic if the little girl next door has more hair than your baby; by the time they are both three or four things should have levelled out and the hair will be indicative of what her adult hair is going to be like.

Caring for a baby's hair and scalp should be a part of the bathing routine. Many mothers are frightened to wash a baby's head because of the soft spot on the top of the head – the fontanelle. Obviously you must take great care until

Above: A budding beauty queen! Pretty hair left to curl naturally; by far the best way to handle this kind of hair.

the bones of the skull knit (usually by eighteen months), but the scalp should be washed. Left untended there is a risk that "cradle cap" could develop. Cradle cap is brown in colour and can start as a small scalp patch which may spread. Normally, it is treated with a little warm – NOT HOT – olive oil on a pad of cotton wool. The warm oil is patted gently over the scalp and

washed off with baby shampoo or baby soap. If you notice this condition developing do check at your clinic as it can also be caused by the baby's diet.

Hopefully, your baby will not have any problems, enjoy bathtime and get used to having her hair washed. Make sure that bathtime is fun time, so use an all-over bodywash and shampoo that does not

1 Five year old Naami has fabulous, long wavy hair, but for play or school it is not very practical to leave it loose.
2 Getting all that hair into a ponytail can be agony. Brush well and then use a wide-spaced comb as you start to gather the hair up. The hand holding the hair should be positioned where the ponytail is to be placed.

couple of times to get them used to the unfamiliar environment, then when the appointment comes around it will be a treat rather than something strange and frightening. Discuss with the stylist what you would like and what would be most suitable; keep it simple for the child's and stylist's sake. Children don't like sitting still and the more complex the haircut the longer it will take. You may be asked to hold your child or keep her attention, so be prepared and take along a favourite toy or game. Should your daughter rebel and become distraught try not to force her and don't be embarrassed: it can't be helped, just go home and try another day.

If you decide to snip at home, do be careful; use only rounded scissors and have someone to help you. Above all, try not to shout at the child; after all, how would you

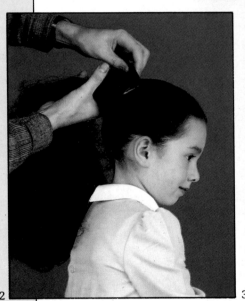

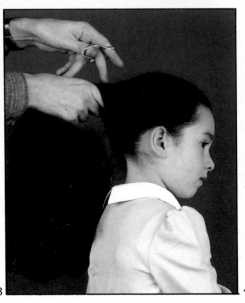

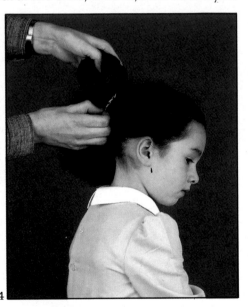

3 Use a covered band held open with your thumb, middle and index finger. Take hold of the hair with these three fingers.
4 Draw the hair through the band. The hand originally holding the hair is now free to hold the band close to the scalp as the ends are drawn through.
5 A simple ponytail which can be left as it is or used as the foundation for various styles.

sting the eyes. Nothing will make a child rebel more in later years than memories of sore, stinging eyes.

Once the hair has grown, try to select a shampoo and conditioner especially for her. Write her name prettily on the bottles so that they become her special things which nobody else uses. Avoid using general, all-purpose family shampoos as these are usually too strong.

Once a reasonable amount of hair has grown, and she is at a fairly controllable age, it's time to start thinking about the first proper haircut. It is important to get children used to the hairdresser at an early age. Some salons specalise in children's hair, with lovely toys and games to keep them amused. Don't worry if your salon does not offer the facilities to entertain children, simply take them to the salon a

like a giant looming over you with what must look like a pair of hedge-cutting shears in their hands.

Getting a child used to the hairdressers will make life much easier for you and, hopefully, will not equate in their minds on the same level as a trip to the dentist.

As your child's hair starts to grow you will start to think about styles. I'm all in favour of keeping children's hair fairly short until they can manage to brush it properly themselves, but I will admit that little girls with long hair look very cute. As a general rule keep hair which is curly or very wavy short, as it tends to tangle very easily and every brushing session becomes agony time for both mother and daughter. Straight hair does not have the same tendency and can be grown longer without too much anguish.

5

1 Twisted three strand plait. Divide the ponytail into three equal sections.
2 Hold each section separately, close to the scalp. Take the right section over into the centre. For a firmer, neater plait twist this section before proceeding.
3 Bring the left hand section over into the centre and twist.
4 Continue working from side to side, remembering to alternate right then left sections into the centre. Don't forget to twist each section as you bring it over.
5 Secure the ends of the plait with another covered band.
6 A pretty, colour-coordinated slide completes the plait. For a special occasion little silk flowers can be pinned around the base and end of the plait.
7 As a variation, the plait can be hoisted into a bun or simply gripped under as shown.
8 For an attractive, alternative way to keep the hair off the face, twist the front hair up and back (like a roll), and secure with hair grips which can be covered with a slide or comb.

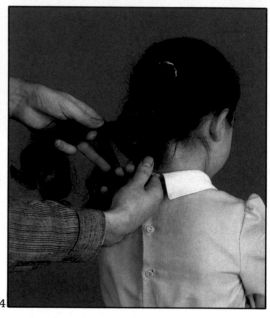

Purchase a good quality brush and comb and always remove all tangles night and morning and, of course, prior to shampooing. Always begin combing at the nape, working from the points to the roots as this is far less painful. For shampooing, follow the directions in the previous chapter, but once conditioner has been applied comb through with a wide-toothed comb before rinsing: this reduces the risk of tangles after the final rinse. Try to dry your child's hair naturally or with a blow dryer on a cool setting, and, as children's hair seems prone to tangles it's a good idea not to rub or tug too much.

Simple hairstyles always work best for children. Fringes should be kept short so as not to obscure vision and long hair should be tied or gripped back. A word on securing long hair: slides are fine but beware of elastic bands; use only the covered type available from most stores and chemists. Plaits and ponytails keep hair neat and tidy but try not to pull them too tight, your child's hair and scalp are still developing and the results of your efforts could be traction alopecia; "hair loss due to undue strain placed on the hair and roots". Would-be little ballet dancers are most susceptible to this condition as their hair is often scraped back into a tight bun. If you must tie it back, tie loosely and not in the same way every day.

Avoid perms at this age however much your eight year old may want curls. I feel that perms and colours should wait until

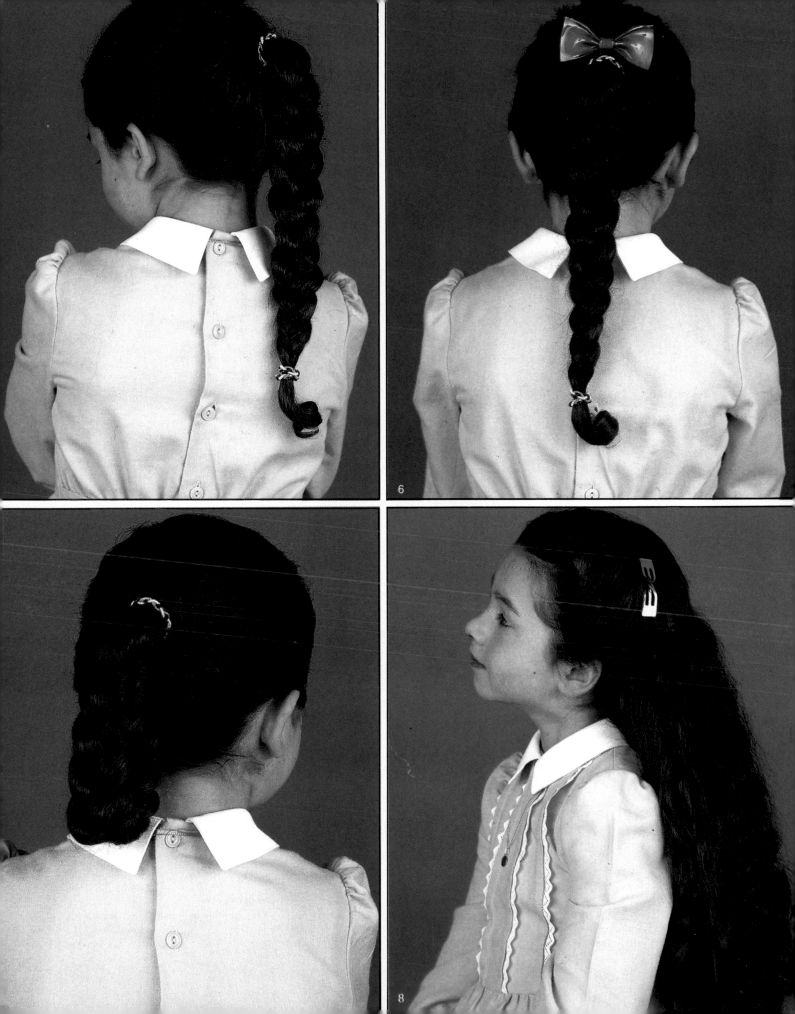

the fourteenth or fifteenth year, when they can cope with the additional attention chemically processed hair demands. The hair and scalp go through quite a few changes in the intervening years, so it's as well to wait.

chemist and they must be used promptly. The shampoos and lotions are easy to apply and will help loosen the nits (eggs) from the hair, but you will have to do the final stage yourself and comb the hair, section by section, with a special, fine-

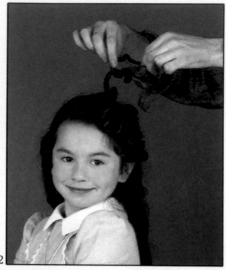
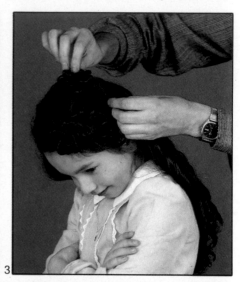

1 The easy way to curls without tears. Work with the hair clean and slightly damp. Part off a small mesh of hair, comb through and begin twisting from roots to points.
2 Keep twisting until the hair coils back on itself.
3 Secure the coil with thick hair pins or grips, close to the scalp. Work all round the head in this manner. Depending on natural curl, leave the coils in for fifteen to thirty minutes.
4 Starting at the nape, remove all grips and pins.
5 Do not brush, but use an Afro-type comb to relax the waves (brushing will result in tangles). Begin at the nape, working from the points of the hair to the roots.

Facing page: pretty dress, pretty girl and an enchanting hairstyle that's quick, easy and painless to achieve.

Keep an eye on children's hair and scalp at all times, particularly if they start to scratch. Nits and lice are all too common and once a child starts school they can spread like wildfire. Naturally, it's upsetting to think of your child being infested, but don't start blaming yourself or your child for being dirty. Nits have little respect for cleanliness and can be found on the most scrupulously-clean children. Treatments can be obtained from your doctor or the

toothed comb until not a trace of the nits remains. *Pediculosis capitis* is the correct term for this condition and it can return again and again, so be on your guard.

It won't be long before your daughter's idea of hairstyle and yours part company, so to avoid problems early on, try to compromise about length and style, in this way everyone stays happy and your nerves remain intact.

CHAPTER 3

Teens to Twenties

1 Toni's face shape and hair texture suit this square, graduated bob, but like many people she needed some tips on blow drying.
2 After shampooing and conditioning, blow-dry lotion is applied to add body and reduce static.

Coping with the psychological and physical changes at puberty can be problematic for both parents and children. For some, the transition from little girl to young lady is relatively smooth, whilst for others it's a battle, when nothing is right and the entire adult world is against you. Understanding what is happening and learning to compromise will help.

back. All this can be very trying when you're so conscious of your appearance and endeavouring to look your best.

If greasy hair is your problem then here are one or two tips that will help:

1. Keep your hair clean: wash every day with a mild shampoo if need be. Follow the advice in chapter 1 for shampooing greasy hair. If your hair is long, then apply

1

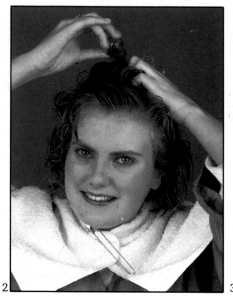

2

3

3 Rough-dry hair to remove excess water.
4 Section hair across from ear to ear, beginning at the nape.
5 Using a radial bristle brush, dry the hair section by section, aiming warm air down the hair shaft.
6 Dry crown hair down, turning just the ends under.
7 To dry the sides, take horizontal partings and keep rotating brush up and down, still maintaining the downward flow of air.

Hormonal changes become apparent as the body shape changes, underarm and pubic hair develops and menstruation begins. Alongside physical development come the fluctuations in mood, swinging from rational behaviour to irrational tantrums so rapidly that it's hard to keep up. This is all normal and we all go through it to a greater or lesser degree.

One of the side effects of this surge in hormonal activity can be the dramatic effect it has on your hair. More often than not hair and skin will become greasy. As the entire glandular system goes into overdrive the sebaceous (oil producing) glands are stimulated, resulting in greasy, lank hair. The skin may also react, becoming very spotty, particularly on the forehead, nose, chin and

conditioner to the middle lengths and ends, do not massage it into the scalp. Don't be put off using conditioner; if long hair is washed frequently the ends will soon become very dry and split.

2. Greasy hair often gives off an unpleasant odour, another reason for keeping hair scrupulously clean, but a change in your diet will also help. Avoid oily, fatty and highly spiced foods; eat as much fresh fruit and vegetables as you can as this will not only help your hair but your skin as well; and say goodbye to junk food, at least until your body has adjusted.

During this time it's a good idea to keep your hairstyle simple and easy to care for; it may be boring but its better to look fairly nice than a total wreck, and you'll soon be

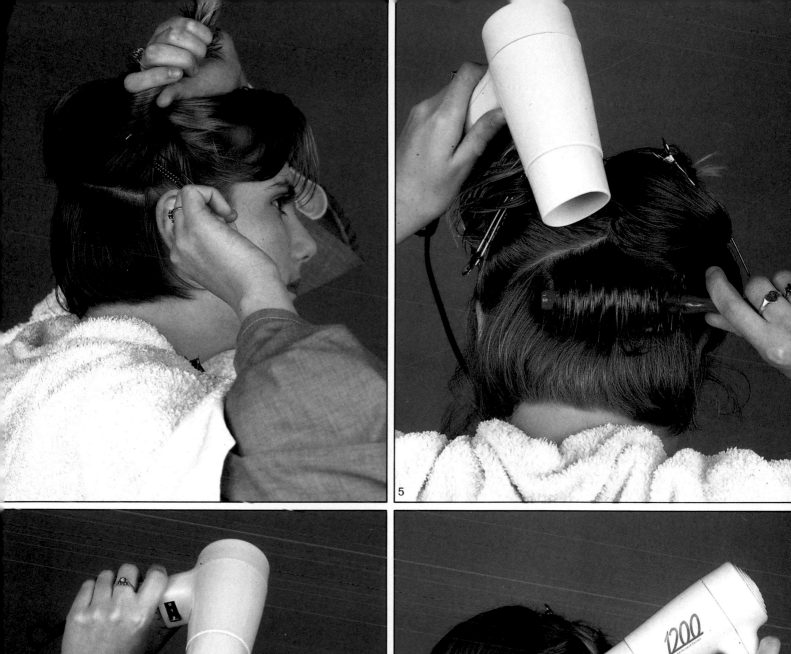

5

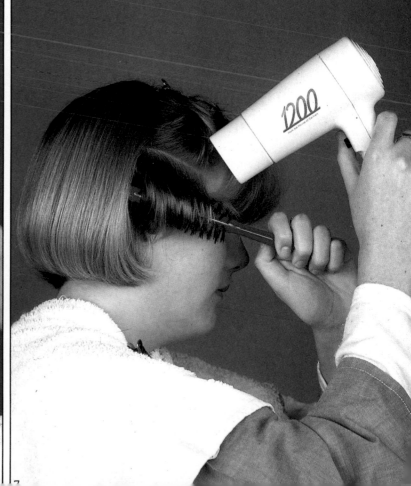

7

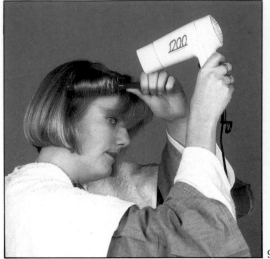

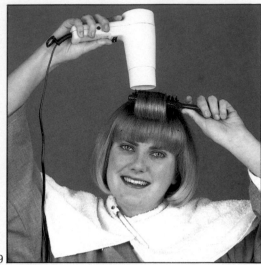

8 Try to ensure that the ends of the hair lie smoothly around the bristle of the brush. Continue up to centre parting.
9 Blow-dry the fringe forward and under. Brush thoroughly to blend all sections.
10 Combination of correct brush control and air flow direction helps to keep the hair smooth and bouncy.

8

9

10

11

11 A lovely style which is perfect for college, work or leisure.
12 A transformation that you too can try. Take a small ponytail just behind the fringe, bind with thick picture hanging wire. Backcomb fringe and ends of ponytail, spray, mould the hair up into shape while sticky and spray again. Emphasise your creation with strategically-placed fluorescent gel. Simple but very effective bob creation.

able to experiment with more adventurous designs. Whenever possible, try to let your hair dry naturally. If you must blow dry then keep the heat down to a minimum; a hot dryer will only stimulate the oil glands further and rigorous brushing spreads the oil through the hair. Unless you're going somewhere special keep greasy hair off your face (especially if you're just lounging around at home), so as not to encourage a spotty skin.

For those still at school there are three main problems you may have to contend with: 1 The hairstyle that you want. 2 The

hairstyle that your parents think suitable. 3 What your school will allow.

Combining all three shouldn't be too difficult: remember, a good haircut is a versatile one. For school and parents your hair can be worn casually but neatly dressed. There is no need for shocking colours that result in suspension, and avant-garde haircuts can wait a while. However, in the evening the simplest style can be transformed with just a little practice and, using gel, you can create outrageous shapes. Backcombed, a tame, innocent haircut can become wild and bold, and

when sprayed with vibrant colour your image changes completely. False swatches of colour or artificial plaits can be gripped in. A good hairdressing salon or chemist will retail coloured sprays and gels which brush or shampoo out, but be careful if your hair is fair as some of the stronger colours do stain the hair. When using coloured sprays it's wise to cover your clothes and stay well away from the furnishings, just in case your aim is not too good. Temporary looks are far more fun, allowing you the flexibility to change your image and mood depending on the situation and clothes you are wearing.

Split ends are a big problem and the only answer is to have them cut off. Try to discourage split ends by going easy with electrical equipment, blow dryers, tongs etc., and do use a good hairbrush, either a bristle type or plastic one which is well finished, with all the quills properly rounded off and no rough edges to tear your hair.

From school to college or the first job is a time when ideas about fashion and image are still developing. The guidelines for the school years still apply, although at college or work the rules are more relaxed, and dress is entirely up to the individual. It's also a time to experiment, trying different clothes, hairstyles, hair colours and make-

need to go out of your way to shock. Assess the kind of place you're going to work in and dress accordingly; save the way-out looks for the evening, you can establish two images – one for work and one for play. When jobs are thin on the ground it's ridiculous to put people off with a very punk hairdo.

1 If you have masses of fine, frizzy hair like Melissa, how about this fun way to make the most of it!
2 Pretty in pastels. Wella Molton Brown Stylers control and define the curl. Top hair is wound conventionally, side and back hair was twisted first for a more rippling wave.
3 No grips, no pins, but what a curl!
4 For a wild look remove Stylers and run your fingers through each curl. Leave loose or pile your hair on top, securing with a few grips or pretty combs.

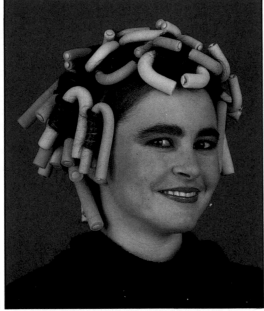

up, finding what suits and what doesn't. Try to co-ordinate clothes rather than buying lots of different bits and bobs that can only be worn individually: it saves money.

Be sensible about hairstyles, especially as far as your job is concerned, as there is no

Whilst establishing an image you'll also be deciding on the type of hairdressing salon you prefer. Initially, most people start by going to the same salon as their mothers, and if this still suits you, fine; if not then you will be looking around. One of the

1 Curly hair is not always the blessing most people imagine it to be and many people – Maria included – would prefer a sleeker, more sophisticated look.
2 Shampoo and condition. An application of hair mousse will help to control that strong curl.
3 Begin at the nape after pinning the rest of the hair well out of the way. Using a tufted, radial bristle brush

best ways to find a good salon is through personal recommendation, so if you see someone whose hair you admire ask them where they had it done; everyone loves a compliment and they are bound to tell you. Otherwise, shop around for a salon that appeals to you from the outside, and go in: does it look as nice on the inside? Explain your requirements to the receptionist and ask for a consultation. A good hairdresser will discuss your hair, your likes and dislikes:

advertisements. Good salons hold regular evening training sessions for juniors and stylists to learn and work out new styles or experiment with the latest looks and products. They are always looking for young people to act as models. The charges are minimal, sometimes free, but you must have plenty of time and be flexible about your style.

Regardless of how, when or where you have your hair done, do keep it clean, and

1

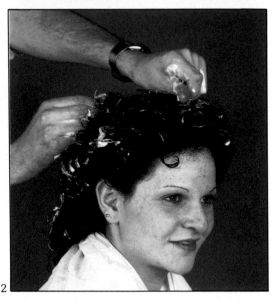
2

for control, take a small section and wrap firmly around the brush. Keeping the hair smooth and taut, unwind the brush as you dry and roll up again. Repeat this procedure, following the brush with the dryer until mesh is dry. Work across nape.
4 & 5 Take the next section from ear to ear, across the back of the head, just below crown.
6 Starting at the centre back, take vertical partings and roll hair in towards middle.

take a picture along of a style you think might suit if it will help you to explain. While you're talking, the hairdresser can assess your personality, how you like to dress and whether you are an introvert or extrovert. If the stylist and staff are interested in your hair you will soon sense it, but if the attitude is one of indifference, leave and continue looking.

If you're continuing your education at college or university or are unemployed, money may be short. One way of getting your hair done cheaply is as a model for salon trainees. Look in the personal column of your local newspaper for

well-cut by a professional. If colours and perms appeal to you then read the relevant chapters in this book to find out when it's safe for you to do it yourself and when you must seek professional help. Eat healthy foods and try to take some exercise: incidentally, dancing is a great form of exercise and fun. You want your hair to last a lifetime so treat it with respect.

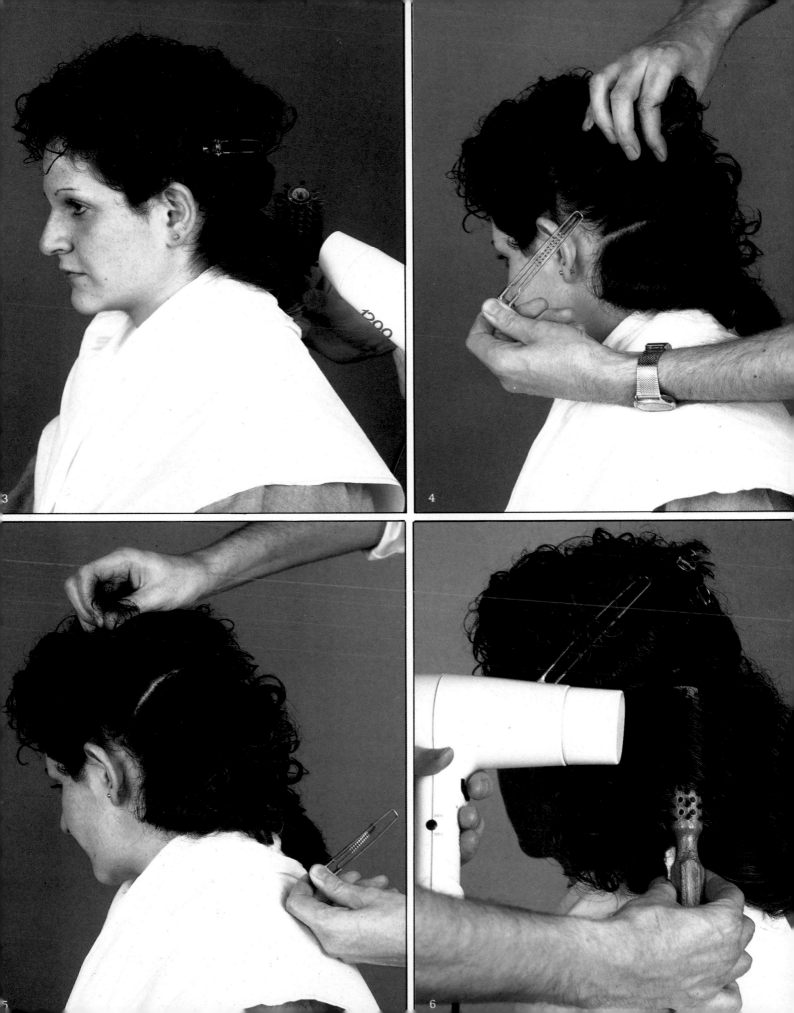

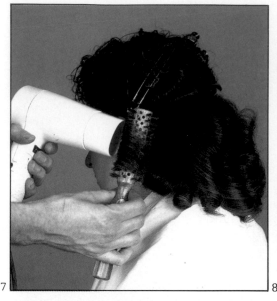

7

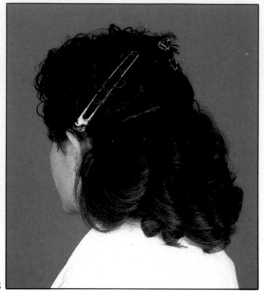

8

7 Work outwards – small section by section – towards the ear. Try to keep hair smooth and taut over the brush. Remember not to overheat the hair.
8 Return to centre back and repeat for the right half, reversing directions. Completed lower back.
9 Section off the top and crown.
10 Dry the top and lower crown hair towards back.
11 For the sides: take diagonal partings and roll the sides up and back, pulling the hair back ever further as you unwind the brush.
12 Front hair is dried over to the side rather than straight back. This will elongate the profile shape and create softness across the forehead.
13 Thoroughly brushed through, and then sprayed lightly with hairspray to protect the hair from moisture. Curls are fun, but it's nice to know that with a little help you, like Maria, can have a more elegant hairstyle.

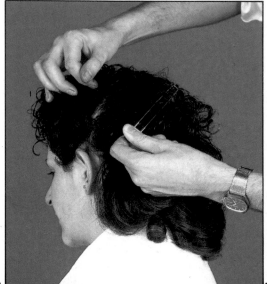

9

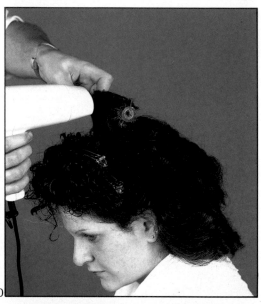

10

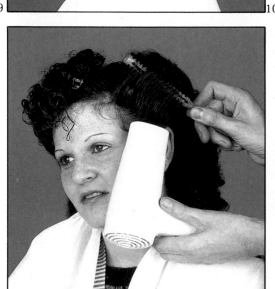

11

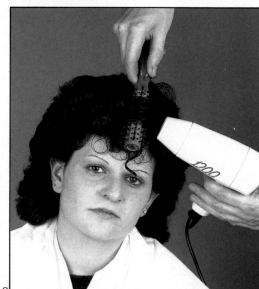

12

13

CHAPTER 4

Curly versus Straight

1 A long face, high forehead and fine, thin hair are three problems Laura has to contend with. Professional help and advice are a must in this case.

Whether our hair is curly or straight it is a paradox of human nature that we will always want the opposite. How well I recall relatives congratulating me on my good fortune at being blessed with curly hair, and my chagrin as a teenager in the late sixties and seventies, when straight hair was "in" and curly hair "out".

correctly assessed and the person doing the perm is competent.

Perming your own hair can be a tricky business, and whenever possible I would advise you to seek professional advice. However, economy measures sometimes have to be taken and a home perm is the only answer.

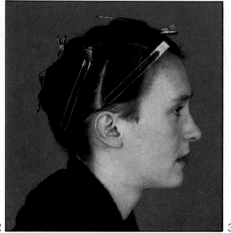

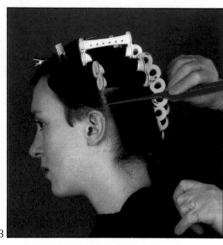

2 After consultation and a haircut, a special pre-perm lotion was applied to protect the hair. Sectioning the hair enables the permer to work methodically.
3 Centre back is wound first, followed by the side sections. Here, the comb indicates the size of the mesh to be parted off.
4 The long back hair is pre-damped with permanent waving lotion, mesh by mesh.
5 End papers protect the points of the hair.
6 The hair is then placed around a large perm curler.
7 The curler is carefully wound down.

Nowadays, hair fashions are far more flexible, with no "in" and "out": the style depends on what suits you and your lifestyle. The majority of people decide that what suits them is a soft, flattering, versatile hairstyle which is easy to manage and will stay looking good from morning until night. For their hair to fulfil these requirements a permanent wave is essential.

Today's permanent waves are many and varied; this applies to both professional products and home perm kits. Some are designed to be used when only a soft result is desired, others for a more conventional curl. Even though they are much safer and more reliable than the perms of old, it must be remembered that the chemicals involved can still cause severe internal structural damage to the hair if misused. Therefore, it is important that the quality of the hair to be permed is

There are certain instances when a professional permanent wave is a must. When your hair is for example:

a Dry or in bad condition
b Tinted
c Bleached
d Highlighted
e Still has the remains of a previous perm in it
f Is one length, or longer than collar length.

In the salon, a good perm technician will take into account any of the above conditions and discuss with you and the stylist the type of perm and degree of curl required to enhance your haircut.

Providing your hair is in a suitable condition to perm, the next step is gently to shampoo and then restyle if necessary. The application of a pre-perm prior to winding will help to protect your hair and act as a buffer to the lotion. Now we come to the

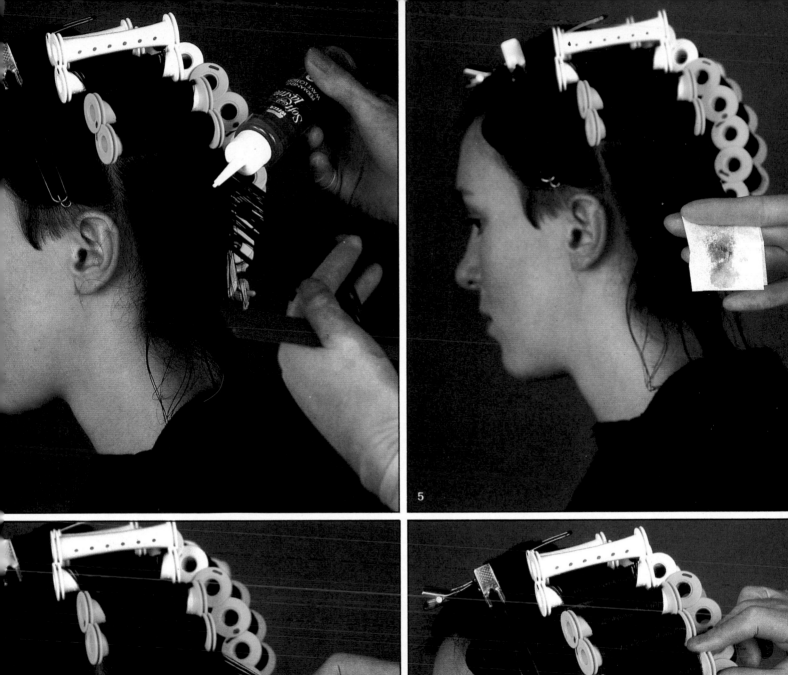

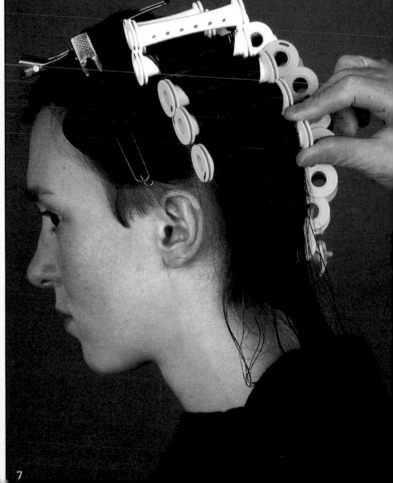

5

7

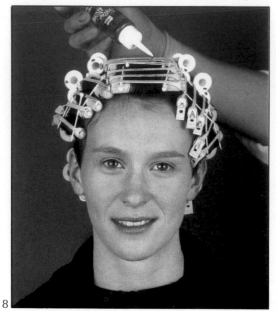

8 On completion, each curler is carefully post-damped with waving lotion.
9 The head is covered with a plastic bag while processing takes place. Once a satisfactory curl can be seen, the hair is rinsed, neutralised and conditioned.

Once all the hair is wound onto curlers and the solution applied, the hair is covered with a plastic cap and left to process. When the desired degree of curl has been reached every curler must be thoroughly rinsed and then blotted with a towel to remove as much water as possible. Now the neutralizer can be applied; this will help to reform the bonds in the cortex into their new wave pattern. After approximately five minutes the curlers are gently removed and more neutralizer sponged onto the ends to ensure all the hair has been properly treated. Rinsing and conditioning complete the process.

For certain styles the hair is also cut after perming, but don't be alarmed that all your curls are going into the dustpan; your hair has been permed from the scalp, and post cutting is used for very short styles, when the finished length would be far too short

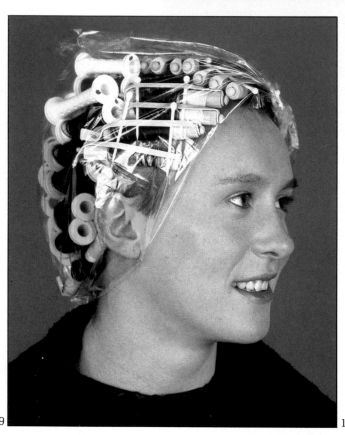

10 The finished perm. The wet curl is bouncy, round and uniform.
11 Gently blow dried to avoid stretching the hair. From fine, limp hair to soft, flattering movement; a professional perm is worth every penny.

serious business: after sectioning, your hair is wound by mesh around the perm rods/curlers, perm solution may be applied as the hair is wound up (pre-damping) or to each perm curler on completion (post-damping).

The choice of a) the lotion and b) the curler is critical; a) relates to the texture and condition of your hair b) to the size of curl required.

to perm, or when a certain effect is required.

As your hair is styled watch the hairdresser and try to pick up some tips. What brushes do they use? Is a styling aid like mousse or gel applied? Can you buy the same product in the salon? Ask questions about home maintenance, what shampoo to use etc.: do you need to damp your hair down every morning (you do with

some styles), how often should you have your hair cut? This information should be volunteered but if it isn't, ASK.

Thinking of a home perm? Then think of your hair first. If it falls into any of the categories previously mentioned, then "don't". Only if you have virgin hair (untreated) in good condition and a fairly short, layered cut should you attempt a home perm.

Choose your home perm kit carefully, read the labels and select one suitable for your hair type and style. It's also preferable to go for a well-known brand name, to have your hair professionally cut beforehand and if your hairdresser is fairly understanding discuss the home perm with him or her.

Before you start, assemble everything you will need and read the directions carefully, at least three times. Enlist the aid of a friend to help you wind the perm, especially the back hair. Follow the

1 To update the bob, perms are almost de-rigeur. For example, Caroline's hair is flat and ordinary.
2 A little movement is introduced with a support perm, wound on Wella's Molton Brown Permers.
3 The wind is directional to complement the finished style. Processing and neutralising follow as before.
4 A scrunch dry encourages the asymmetric shape without distorting the curl. Perfect easycare wash-and-wear style for the modern girl.

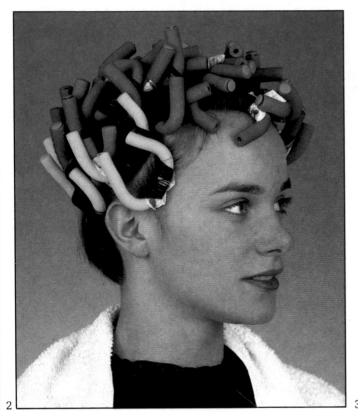

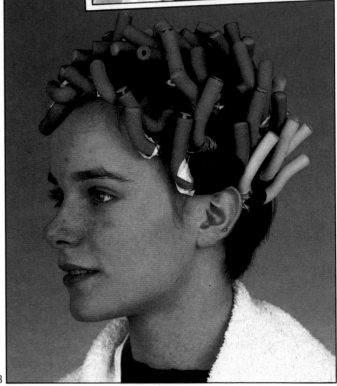

directions implicitly. They are the result of years of research and not to be disregarded. If you're at all doubtful about the result, carry out a test curl: you will find instructions on how to do this in the pack.

WARNING – do remember to keep these products away from children and, once you have finished, dispose of any left-over lotions safely.

Drying: the perfect way to dry freshly permed hair is naturally, as the less tension and strain put on the hair the better, but, if you prefer to blow dry do so gently; don't pull, stretch or overheat each strand. Give your hair a chance to settle down first, you'll find the perm will last longer.

In the unfortunate event that something goes wrong, go back to your

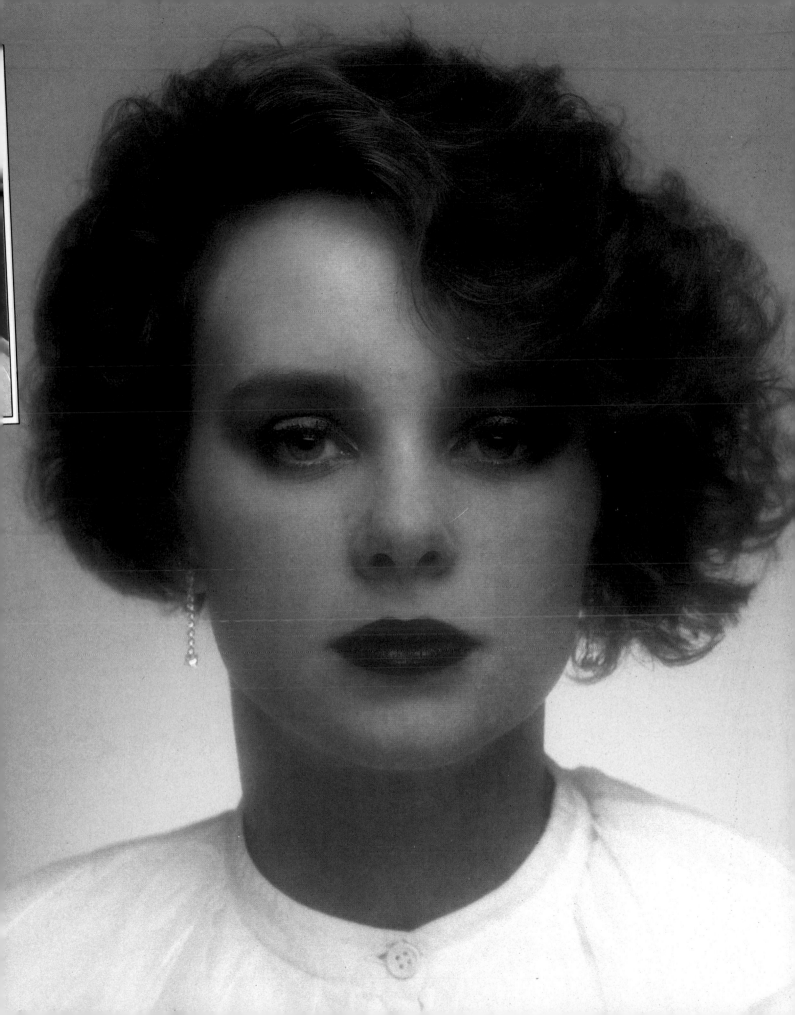

1 Short, straight hair that lacks style and shape, Jenny's hair is perfect for the bodywave.
2 As the hair was so short only the top was permed, employing a weaving technique for a very natural result. To ensure a good blend with straight hair, side and back curls were positioned vertically.
3 Nape and sides cropped after perming. Top is dried with the fingers, and a little gel accentuates the feathery fringe.
4 A simple but very effective short hair design.

1

hairdresser and tell them everything you have done to your hair. Unless they are completely in the picture, repairing the damage could be difficult.

Whether you have a home or salon perm, the hair must be carefully treated, regularly conditioned and cut to keep the curl at its best. Avoid permanent colours for ten to fourteen days before and after perming. A good, normal perm should last until it is cut out of the hair, although it will start to loosen close to the scalp as the hair grows through. You may feel like hanging onto your perm and avoid haircuts, but the longer and tattier it gets the more the extra length and weight will pull your hair flat. Cutting every four to six weeks will prolong the life of your perm rather than decrease it.

In the salon you will hear lots of different terms bandied about to describe various perming techniques. These

2

3

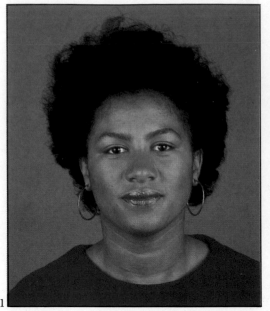

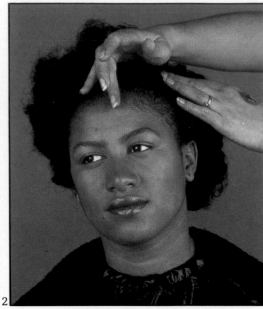

1 Chemical relaxing will make Sandra's frizzy hair more amenable to current popular styling methods.
2 First the hair and scalp are checked for breakage and abrasions. For protection, a special conditioning gel is applied to the hair and hairline.
3 Four sections make application easier and more efficient for the technician.
4 A small mesh is parted off at the nape and held down.

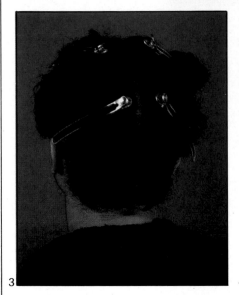

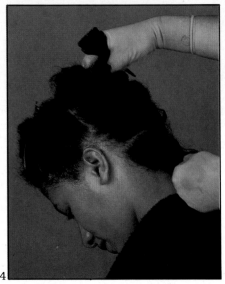

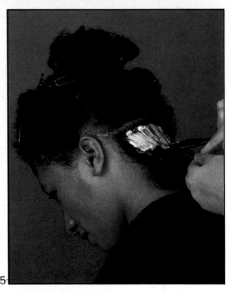

5 Relaxer is applied, with a brush, to the hair (not the scalp).
6 One back section complete.
7 Once both back sections have been treated it's time to move to the top. Application begins at the crown and works forward.
8 The front hairline is very delicate so it is treated last of all.
9 Finally, all the hair is gently smoothed mesh by mesh.

techniques are used to create certain effects. If one is to be used on your hair and you don't understand what they are talking about, try not to sink further into the chair whilst nodding your head sagely in agreement, speak up and ask for an explanation. It's so important that you and the permer are on the same wavelength. Here are just a few techniques that may sound familiar:

Perm wrap – another way to describe winding a perm.

Directional perm – instead of a conventional wrap the hair is permed to follow the lines of the finished style.

Root perm – normally used on fairly short hair. Hair at the roots is wound around the perm curler and the ends left straight. Very casual effect for root lift only.

Body/Support perms – very soft curl or bend is put into the hair. The result is very natural and easy to manage. This type may need doing more often than a conventional perm.

Partial perm – used when just part of the hair, like the top or back, requires perming. For example, the underneath nape hair could be permed to help a one length bob turn up or under.

Perm curler, Perm rod – one and the same thing.

Black Hair. Special perms for black hair are a fairly recent innovation, although many of us have been adapting conventional perming methods to suit very curly hair for some years. Since these perms first came onto the market there have been vast improvements and now the technique

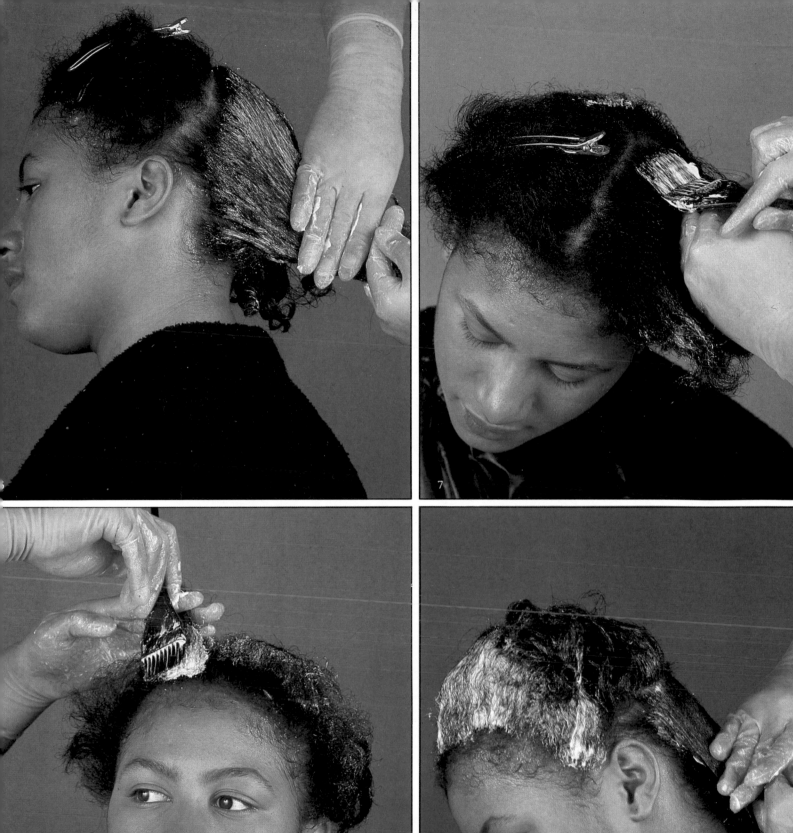
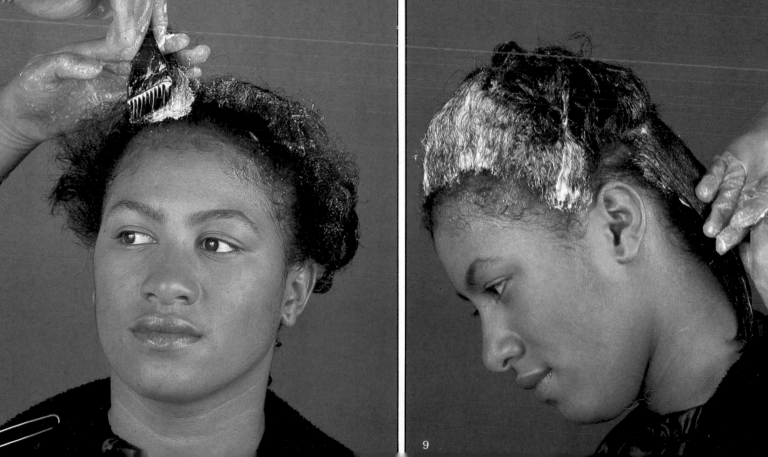

is very similar to that used for Caucasian hair, except that the very tight curl is being realigned into a soft, manageable curl that can be easily set, blow dried or left natural. For hairdressers and consumers this has been an extremely exciting time for black hair, and at last we have the versatility to change styles easily.

Relaxing is the modern term for straightening hair: we no longer try to get hair bone-straight as this can be continued afterwards to help repair and replace moisture and oils that may have removed by the process.

One of the biggest problems is a dry scalp and dry hair, so make sure you invest in a can of moisturising oil sheen spray. As a rule, salons specialising in black hair design carry a good range of professional hair care products for retail, and the stylists are only too happy to advise you on home maintenance.

After relaxing, Sandra's hair was neutralised (to fix in the sleeker pattern), conditioned and cut. It should be noted that this is a skilled professional service.
Facing page: a straightforward blow-dry, plus a little additional work with the curling tongs and 'Voila!', Sandra can now wear her hair in a variety of fashionable styles.
Right: backcombing and hair spray enlarges the shape for a more exaggerated style. Whatever your style preference, make sure your stylist explains the aftercare routine for relaxed or permed hair.

detrimental. It is a process that I feel should only be carried out in the salon. New and better products are continually being developed, but the risk factor is still there, particularly as black hair is so very delicate and brittle. If you must relax your hair at home please be very careful and follow the directions.

It is a good idea to prepare your hair for any chemical process. Build up the condition by applying regular protein packs for three or four weeks prior to a perm or relaxer. This should also be

Finally, the female of our species is not the only one to reap the benefits of modern perming techniques; men have also jumped on the band-wagon. It began mostly with sportsmen, who found the idea of easy care "wash and wear" looks ideal. Others quickly followed suit, finding that soft perms made hair look thicker and also easier to blow dry. Perming a man's hair is no different to perming a woman's, except that the finished style is obviously more masculine.

Your Hair during Pregnancy

A healthy, pregnant woman has a beauty and serenity all of her own, whether it's from a sense of fulfillment or pride in the new life growing inside her is hard to define, but one thing is certain: mums-to-be do have a certain radiance.

Obviously, your health prior to conception, during pregnancy, and after, are the prime concerns of your doctor and

From my own observations and discussions with other hairdressers I've found that very little advice is offered to people other than "its because you're pregnant" or, "wait until your body settles down". Such platitudes are fine, but a little more explanation would not go amiss.

The first trimester: most people will tell you that during pregnancy your hair and

Right: in her seventh month of pregnancy, Norma's hair is in superb condition, although somewhat out of shape. Far right and facing page: restyled into clean, simple lines – the perfect hair to show off a classic cut.

gynaecologist. Your diet will be checked and revised if necessary; your general health monitored throughout the term, and it goes without saying that smoking, drinking and the taking of unprescribed drugs are taboo. But with all this advice, where is there anything but a passing reference to your hair? Do people assume that you are not going to bother about it for the next nine months, or that changes in the way your hair looks and feels at this time are not important?

Whilst hair will not be the number one priority it still plays a major psychological role in that the better it looks, the better you feel.

skin will be at their peak, with shining hair and glowing skin. In reality this could be quite the opposite for the first three months. Apart from morning sickness making you look and feel wretched, the sudden increase in hormone activity may also affect the sebaceous glands, resulting in a greasy skin and lank, oily hair. A mild, hypo-allergenic cleanser and toner should help the skin and, as for the hair, shampoo as often as required with a mild shampoo. Don't go mad and have all your hair cut off because you're fed up; the grease problem should soon abate.

The second trimester: by this stage your body should have adjusted and you will

feel at peace with yourself; people will begin to tell you how marvellous you look and your skin and hair will be smooth and manageable respectively. You may even notice that your hair seems thicker and grows more quickly; this is quite possible and once again it is influenced by the increase in hormone levels. Feeling as you do, the temptation will be to rush out and completely change your hair, but stop and think seriously before you do anything drastic. By all means experiment with new styles, but remember that as you get larger

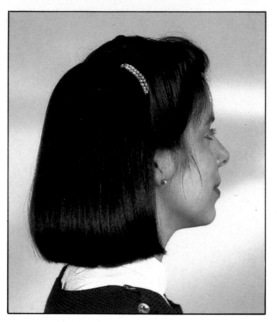

and your energy level decreases you will feel less inclined to fiddle with a complicated hairstyle that takes an hour a day to make it look presentable. Opt for a good, versatile haircut that can be dressed in different ways and is easy to manage. In the early stages, if your hair is in good condition a perm can be a blessing, but only have one if your hairdresser says it's OK. Many hairdressers prefer not to perm your hair during pregnancy, especially in the later months, so be guided by their advice.

Paradoxically, some people notice that their hair falls out more at this time. If you suspect you're losing excessive amounts, consult your doctor.

The third trimester: nearing the end of your term you will probably feel more tired, and this is normal. Prone to back ache, etc., you'll worry about your appearance but feel less inclined to spend a lot of time on your hair. It's crucial that you pamper yourself, so maintain your visits to the hairdresser, whether it's for a regular four to six weekly haircut or a weekly shampoo and blow dry.

Throughout your pregnancy ensure that you regularly shampoo and condition your hair, adjusting the products you use to suit your hair as it changes from greasy to normal or dry. Do not stick to the same products if your hair and scalp alter. If you shampoo at home get someone to help, leaning over a bath or basin is a tricky business in the later months and may make you feel dizzy so it's advisable to have a helping hand.

General advice: tell your hairdresser on your next visit to the salon that you are pregnant so that they can keep an eye on the condition of your hair. As I have already mentioned, be guided by them with regards to chemical processes such as perming and colouring. If your hair is already tinted, then obviously you must keep up regrowth applications or your hair will look unsightly.

The baby: believe it or not the amount of hair your baby will have is determined in the womb. The scalp of the unborn child is the centre of much activity as the epidermis indents to form the hair follicle, and at the same time cellular action is taking place to create the papilla. The first hairs will be of the lanugo type (fine downy hair), this will soon be shed, sometimes before birth or just after. Gradually, new, more recognisable hair will grow and those follicles will continue to produce hair after hair after hair, hopefully for a lifetime.

After pregnancy: hair grows in cycles. Basically there is a growing cycle and a resting cycle. During pregnancy the growth cycle is longer and normal hair loss during the resting stage decreases. Once the baby is born the pregnancy-induced hormones plummet, and this may result in a substantial increase in hair loss which can seem alarming. But really you are only shedding the normal amount plus the hair you should have lost during pregnancy. This will occur around three to six months after the birth, although it has been known to continue on and off for a couple of years. The hair and scalp will gradually return to normal, so just be patient. However, if you are worried ask your doctor for advice or go to a qualified trichologist.

As we have discussed in previous chapters, your diet and general health can have dramatic repercussions on your hair, now more than ever. Make sure that you eat properly and try to get plenty of rest in-between baby feeds and nappy changing. It won't be long before you're slipping back into your tightest jeans and thinking of a new hairstyle.

CHAPTER 6

Colour Wise

Top right: Haley would love to experiment with colour, but nothing too shocking or permanent.
Below: mahogany coloured styling mousse will add warmth and interest.
Below right: just a hint of red that attractively catches the light.
Facing page: fashionable, high, spiky front that emphasises the colour even more.

Not so long ago, any woman who coloured her hair – unless she was a movie star – would be labelled a "scarlet woman". Perhaps this was due to the rather unsubtle colours available: red, blonde or black. Artificially-coloured hair looked just that, artificial. The results were unpredictable, as many young women found out to their cost. Fortunately, this is no longer the case and today, we can choose from a wide range of colours, all designed to give a natural result and leave the hair in good condition. Not only do we have natural-looking shades to choose from but also

some vivid, vibrant hues that nature never dreamed of: rich burgundies, bright reds, blues and fuchsias, to name but a few. In fact, anything goes, but before you reach for your coat and dash out to the nearest hairdresser or chemist let us consider a few important points.

Right: not only was Sharon's hair very out of shape, but an experiment with colour had left her with the legacy of a two inch regrowth.

Below: a semi-permanent colour, 'Black Cherry', helped to camouflage the regrowth. Applied like a shampoo, the colour has not only blended-in the regrowth but added a lovely rich tone and sheen to the hair.

Facing page: rainbow hues for artistic colouring.

1. Before you contemplate any form of colour, ensure that your hair is in good condition. Do not colour it yourself if it is dry, brittle or damaged in any way, but seek professional advice.

2. Do not attempt to bleach or recolour bleached hair to its natural shade yourself.

3. If your hair is permanently waved, relaxed or already tinted, once again you should go to the hairdresser.

4. If you are fed up with your present artificial colour do not attempt to remove/strip it yourself; go to the experts.

5. Do consider the cost before embarking on any form of colour change. Some colouring techniques are expensive and may require retouching every three to four weeks. Make sure you can afford the upkeep.

1 Pale blonde hair requires a fair amount of maintenance. For example, Sonia regularly has to have her regrowth lightened.
2 Bleaching just the root area can be more tricky than treating the entire head. Great care must be taken not to overlap the bleach onto previously lightened hair.

complexion lightens, and going darker will only emphasize the ageing process, resulting in a harsh, unnatural look.

Colour Types Temporary colours, as the name implies, last from shampoo to shampoo. They coat the outside of the shaft and can be used to even out colour in salt-and-pepper hair, or to improve the appearance of white hair that has a yellow, dingy look to it. This type of colour will also enhance the natural glints in hair: for example, a mahogany temporary colour on a natural medium brown base will add rich, warm lights.

This type of colour is available from most chemists and hairdressers. Generally, it is sold in small, individual bottles as a temporary colour and setting lotion combined. The latest innovation of foam-type temporary colours are great for those

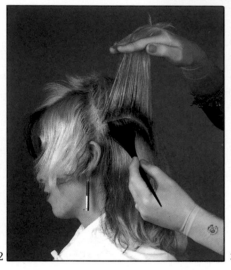

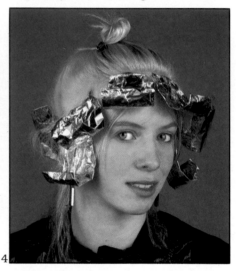

3 Bleach has been meticulously applied to the new growth. Previously bleached hair is lifted away from the head.
4 Once the roots have lifted the bleach is removed. The foil packs contain fine meshes of hair treated with black tint.
5 This process adds body and texture to Sonia's fine hair and once scrunch dried, the black meshes feather back for that extra flair.

Colour Choice If you are considering colouring your hair at home, keep it simple. It is advisable only to lighten or darken your hair one or two shades with a permanent tint, or use a semi-permanent colour to enhance the natural glints.

Colours should complement your skin: this includes how light or dark you are going and whether the tone, e.g. red, gold, ash or violet, is warm or cool.

A golden tone will add warmth to a pale skin. Florid complexioned? Then avoid warm tones and opt for more neutral or ashen shades. Olive skins can take very dark shades, but be careful of choosing a colour with a very red or gold tone as this can make the skin look sallow.

Mature gracefully if you're naturally dark and going grey, and resist the temptation to colour you hair back to its natural brunette. As we age, the skin tone changes, small facial lines appear and the

of you who prefer naturally to dry or blow dry your hair. These can be purchased from some hairdressing salons.

To apply, towel blot your hair after shampooing and, if using the liquid kind, sprinkle the contents of the bottle evenly over your hair whilst massaging the colour through with your free hand. Be careful not to tip the entire contents of the bottle onto the top of your head, especially if your hair is porous, as you could end up looking like a piebald pony.

For the foam variety, expell an orange-sized amount of the foam into the palm of your hand and massage it evenly through your hair: use a little more if your hair is fairly long.

Unfortunately, the drawback with this type of colour is that it rubs off on collars, brushes and pillowcases, and if you accidentally get caught in a shower without your brolly the colour may run.

5

Semi-Permanents Semi-permanents are a great way to introduce yourself to colour. Modern semi-permanents are a far cry from the sixties products; they last longer and the colour range is far greater. Lasting from six to eight shampoos, the conditioning agents in the colour leave the hair remarkably shiny and bouncy.

Above: if you can't make up your mind whether to go light or dark, compromise; like Sonia you can have the best of both worlds.
Facing page: a casual, upswept design that proves how stunning bleached hair can look.

The colour itself penetrates into the cuticle, unlike a temporary colour which merely coats the hair. Certain ranges of semi-permanents are specifically designed to cover grey hair and do so fairly successfully. Others are designed to produce fashion shades – rich reds, burgundies or golds. These should not be applied to white hair, which could turn very pink or yellow. One thing a semi-permanent will not do is lighten your hair; it can only enhance your natural shade, cover grey or make hair darker. Always check the manufacturers "colour choice guide" and don't be misled by the words "shampoo in colour". If it claims that it will make you hair lighter then it is a permanent tint. You can check inside the pack and if there are two bottles which have to be mixed together then, once again, it is a permanent colour.

If your hair is already tinted but fades in-between root retouches, a semi-colour of a similar tone can be used to boost the colour; do not attempt this yourself but ask your hairdresser. Before applying, carry out a strand and skin test: you will find instructions on how to do this in the directions enclosed in the packet.

Assemble everything you will need before you start and take the phone off the hook unless you want a coloured phone as well. You will need plenty of old towels and it's a good idea to cover the floor and work tops with paper, just in case things get messy. Wear gloves to apply to either clean, dry hair or shampooed, towel-dried hair (check instructions); massage evenly through the hair and cover with a plastic cap if necessary; allow to develop and remove as directed. If your skin is dry and porous it's a good idea to apply a thin layer of barrier cream or vaseline close to the hair line to prevent skin staining. After removal dry and style your hair as normal.

Permanent Colour Permanent colours are just that – permanent – and once in the hair they can only be removed by cutting the colour out as the hair grows. Professional colourists can remove artificial colour, but it is a long and expensive business.

Permanent colours can lighten, darken, cover grey and add a variety of tones to the hair. Permanent colours actually penetrate into the cortex of the hair, working on the natural colour molecules (melanocytes) and depositing colour.

Permanent colours for home use usually come in an oil form. In a pack you will find one bottle of colour and one bottle of hydrogen peroxide which, when mixed together, form an oil-like gel. Normally, I recommend that all permanent tints are carried out by a professional colourist, but if for economic reasons you prefer to colour at home, give considerable thought to colour selection and always choose a well-known, reputable brand.

You can go as dark as you like with a permanent colour as long as it suits you. When going lighter, choose a colour only one or two shades lighter than your natural hair. If you lighten any further, your natural tones will have a marked effect on the end result. If you are covering grey hair then stick to a fairly neutral colour: leave the fashion shades to the hairdresser.

Application: remember to carry out a strand and skin test as per the manufacturer's directions. Assemble everything you will need (see semi-

Right: and now for something completely different. Firstly, Imogen's hair was cut and blow-dried to style. Bleach was stippled onto the ends of the top hair and applied to the longer meshes behind the ears. With the bleach removed, a mid-burgundy tint was applied through top and back, omitting the long, bleached meshes. The sides and tips of fringe are tinted blue-black. Below and facing page: the incandescent effect of the bleach under the burgundy hair catches the light beautifully – a different and distinctive effect that shows just how well curling and colouring go together.

colours). Each manufacturer's directions will vary slightly, so read them carefully before you begin. Some will imply that for a first-time application the colour is massaged through the hair like a shampoo, allowed to develop and removed. This is fine if you're going darker, but going lighter requires a little more care.

To tint the hair lighter enlist the help of a friend. The prepared tint must be applied methodically, mesh by mesh, to the middle lengths and ends of the hair, approximately an inch from the root. This is because tint will take quicker on the hair closest to the scalp, partly because of body heat, and if the colour is applied to the root area first, an uneven colour will result. Once the middle lengths and ends begin to lift (about fifteen minutes), apply tint to the roots and ensure that all the hair is covered. Develop for the recommended time.

To remove, add water and lather up the tint as much as possible, rinse thoroughly, shampoo lightly, condition and style as normal. Do not try to keep any left-over tint: once mixed it cannot be kept and must be thrown away. Safety first: if any tint goes into the eyes rinse IMMEDIATELY with cold water. Seek medical advice if any irritation results. Keep all products away from children.

Regrowths Hair grows approximately half an inch a month. This new growth will require attention every four weeks, more often if there is a marked difference between your tinted and natural hair. Prepare as before – don't forget to carry out a skin test. Section and apply colour to the new growth only, and allow to develop. If the lengths and ends are faded, then

massage the remaining colour through the hair for the last five minutes or so. Remove as before.

This guide to permanent tinting is very general: do read directions carefully and keep them handy as you work. If in doubt, go to the hairdressers and leave well alone.

Henna Henna has its pluses and minuses; on the plus side it is eminently suitable for people who are allergic to other forms of manufactured colour preparations, while on the minus side it can be messy to apply and the results unpredictable.

Henna is produced from the powdered leaves of *Lawsonia Inermis*, a native shrub of the Far East, Middle East and Asia. It has been in and out of favour since Cleopatra first dipped her dainty toe in the Nile. The sixties in particular heralded a rebirth for henna, when everyone went back to nature and natural products. Since then its popularity as a colour has waned somewhat, but henna shampoos and conditioners have remained a firm favourite.

Natural additives can vary the shades henna will produce, from indigo for black to woad for chestnut. The country of origin is also important as different growing conditions affect the quality of the henna.

Henna is a permanent vegetable colour and works by both penetrating and coating the hair; it will also leave hair very shiny. Never use henna on very dry, permed or tinted hair. For best results the base shade should be naturally medium to dark brown. To apply: follow the directions carefully and take care to protect yourself and your surroundings – remember, it can be messy. Apply barrier cream close to hairline. Mix the henna powder with hot water in a large mixing bowl. Section the hair and apply the henna with your fingers, massaging it thoroughly through each section. Work quickly and if the henna starts to dry out in the bowl add some more hot water. When all the hair has been treated, cover with foil and leave to develop. Development time can be halved by going under a warm hood dryer. Clear up as soon as you can – you don't want henna walked all over the house!

When you're ready to remove the colour, lean over a basin before removing the foil so that any loose powder falls into the bowl. Rinse and rinse again, shampoo and rinse once more, and repeat if hair still feels gritty. Be prepared for fifteen minutes of rinsing and shampooing before it's all gone. Style in your normal way; the finished result should be very, very shiny with a good, deep, rich colour.

Words of advice: do not use henna on fair hair. Do not henna over tinted or permed hair yourself, and do not attempt permanently to wave or permanently tint hennaed hair, but go to the hairdresser.

Bleaching To bleach the hair means removing all the natural colour pigment: it is a strong process and one which should only be undertaken by a professional colourist.

Bleached hair is showing signs of making a come-back, especially with young people into "street fashions". Some of the looks around are very strong, and bleached, pale blonde hair can certainly be dramatic.

For the more conservative among us, completely bleaching your hair should only be contemplated if you have naturally dark blonde or lighter hair and if your complexion can take it. At the same time you must consider the condition of your hair, the time it will consume (retouching every three weeks), and the cost.

If bleaching is for you then keep the style short, apply protein packs regularly and always use a cream rinse after shampooing to close the cuticle. Perming is OUT, sometimes it works on bleached hair and sometimes not, so concentrate instead on the three C's – cut, colour and condition.

Highlights: these are fine meshes of hair which are bleached or tinted to create a sunlightened effect.

Lowlights: fine meshes of hair which are tinted darker to add colour or introduce a warm tone to the hair.

Naturalising: once again fine meshes of hair are tinted, but this time three or four colours from, maybe, copper to mahogany are used. As the hair moves the colours catch the light, adding depth and interest.

These are just a sample of the technical terms you may come across. The methods employed are all similar; sometimes strands of hair will be pulled through a special self-sealing cap with a fine hook; these strands are then bleached or tinted, or the strands will be methodically and individually woven out, coloured, and wrapped in foil or cling film.

Other techniques include hairpainting: applying colour stratically to emphasize the lines of a style; two or three tone effects where large area of hair are coloured, for example, from dark blonde at the nape, getting progressively lighter towards the

Contrasting styles, but both equally eye-catching. Right: a sleek, classic style subtly coloured for maximum effect and (facing page) dramatic blue-black colouring complements a chic, feathery bob style.

crown; finger or touch colours, where colours are applied with the tips of the fingers or comb to enhance a style, or you could go really mad and have a large mesh of hair bleached and then coloured turquoise, violet or brilliant, poppy red. Providing it's properly done, crazy colours can be great fun.

Whatever your colour choice, from the sublime to the ridiculous, make sure it suits you and your lifestyle. Choose with care and if you're in the salon make sure you fully understand what the colourist is going to do, how often it will need retouching and the cost.

CHAPTER 7
The Era of Change

Facing page: a blaze of colour: fabulous, natural red hair cut to complement the natural curl. Nature at her best.

Thank goodness the days are fast disappearing when a woman was considered "over the hill" at thirty-five, or as soon as she had produced the required quota of children. Now, a woman in her forties can be as glamorous as her twenty-year-old daughter.

A higher standard of living, magazines, television and the economic climate have done much to bridge the age barrier. Let me expand on this theory. In the Western world our diet has improved considerably and those of us concerned about our looks and well-being have kicked the junk food habit and are into a more sensible, well-balanced diet. As I mentioned earlier, healthy hair and skin come from within.

Magazines and TV bombard us with features on apparently ageless women, and not just the rich and famous nor those who have undergone plastic surgery. We regularly read features about seemingly dowdy women of all ages who are transformed by a new hairdo, make-up and clothes. Admittedly they had expert advice, but with a little time and patience you too could present a different image to your family and friends.

More and more of us continue to work after marriage, and mothers pursue their careers whilst managing a home and children, or they return to work once children are of school age. In today's tough economic climate the majority of people have to work, but this need to work has gone some way towards encouraging us to take more care of ourselves. Hair, clothes and make-up are kept as stylish and fashionable as our purses will allow, and in the long run hair is, perhaps, one of the cheapest ways of keeping yourself up to date.

Staying "in vogue". One of the best ways of keeping a check on yourself at any age requires very little expense, just time, a good mirror and a few old photographs dating back over the last couple of years. Look at your hair, clothes and make-up in the pictures and then compare this with your reflected image. Clothes have probably changed according to fashion, but has you hair and make-up? Nothing dates you more than these two things. It is so easy and comfortable to stay with a hairstyle that suited you ten years ago, and to change your make-up requires experimentation and practice. Changing your hair and make-up first thing in the morning when you're dashing off to work is not the best time. We can all find a little time in the evenings to try something new.

Updating your hairstyle may mean nothing more than blowdrying instead of setting, or dressing your hair in a softer or sleeker way. Changes come more expensive if a restyle, permanent wave or colour are required, but presumably everyone has their hair cut regularly and a perm or colour won't need doing every week, so the extra expense can be budgeted for. The boost a new style can give you far out-weighs the financial outlay, especially when friends and loved ones start telling you how much younger you look. The only drawback to this is when you start to wonder what you have been looking like for the past few years if you look so much better now!

Remember, too, that a new hairdo is a great confidence and morale booster, so if you are searching for a new job, or returning to work, put a new hairstyle at the top of your list of things to do before interview day.

Twenties: by now you will have left the problems of puberty and adolescence behind you, but your hair and skin will continue to change as you age. In the twenties everything should be at its peak: hair, skin and general health. Hormonal disturbances at the onset of puberty will have levelled out, although your hair can still become unruly or greasy prior to menstruation. Unfortunately, the twenties can also be a time when we are so keen to do and try everything that we abuse our

1 Vivienne has pretty, dark golden blonde hair with masses of natural movement. Here we show how to make the most of wavy hair with a scrunch dry.

2 After shampooing and conditioning, hair gel is used to give body and bounce. Massage the gel well into the root area and then comb through to ends.

always protect your hair with a sunhat, scarf or a conditioner which blocks out the harmful rays of the sun. Shampoo and condition after swimming, and be especially careful if your hair is chemically processed in any way.

General care of your hair at this time should be simple. Shampoo as you feel necessary; if it is every day choose a mild shampoo. If your hair is permed, tinted or relaxed, choose one that is formulated for those conditions. Regular use of conditioners goes without saying.

Into the thirties: it's a sad fact that from now on everything is going into decline, your skin and muscle tone are not as elastic, your hair is not as bouncy or naturally shiny as it once was. But before you decide to leap off the nearest bridge – stop – think positively,

3 Rough-dry hair and push it all forward. Begin at the nape, opening your fingers like a claw.

4 Lift and scrunch the hair up with your fingers. Keep opening and closing your fist to allow the air to circulate.

5 Sides – dry roots upwards and then scrunch ends.

6 Slide the fingers into front hair, moving the hair up and to the side; scrunch ends.

7 Drying complete. Run fingers up through hair to ensure roots are dry. That's all there is to it.

8 Completed back view.

bodies with crash diets, lack of proper exercise and sleep, and our hair comes under attack as we experiment with hair colours, perms and tortuous hairstyles. Remember: all things in moderation.

Nervous disorders and high stress situations can also have dramatic repercussions on our hair and as the twenties can be a traumatic time in affairs of the heart you may experience some adverse hair reaction purely because of emotional stress. Getting married can be exciting but exhausting, so at this time be sensible and eat properly; don't crash diet, and get plenty of rest.

This is also a time when sunbathing is a must and the browner you are the better you look and feel. It seems hard to believe the effect that sun and sea can have on your hair and skin when you look so good, but think of the future; damage done now to the skin is irreparable, and the hair too must be protected. When sunbathing

you know you will have to exercise and maybe diet more strictly than before, but equally you should be more at ease with yourself, more self-assured and confident. The physical changes are gradual, which makes them easier to cope with. At the risk of repeating myself, healthy diet and exercise are a must, no matter how hectic your schedule. If you smoke or drink a lot cut down now; smoking only encourages the small lines around your eyes, deprives cells of oxygen and makes your hair smell terrible.

One thing you may notice about your hair is a tendency towards dryness, even if it was greasy in your teens. As with the skin, the sebaceous glands are not as active as they once were, therefore the hair and skin are not receiving as much natural oil and moisture. Indications may be dry, dull, flyaway hair, or a feeling of coarseness. Be aware of what is happening and adjust your shampoo and conditioning routine

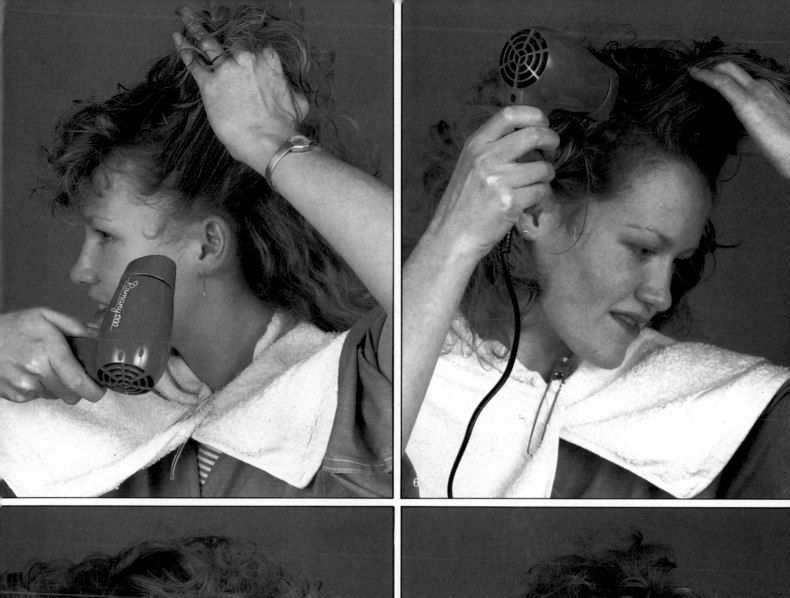

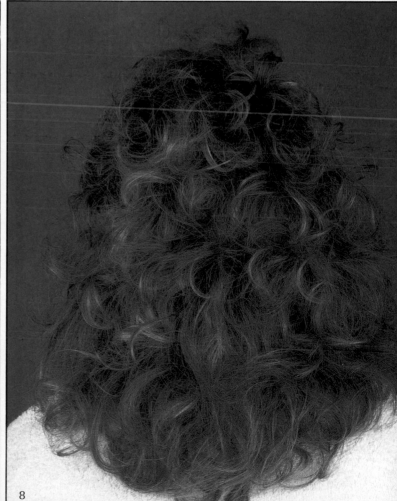

8

For more fullness the hair can be backcombed.

1 Beginning at the top, part off a small mesh of hair no wider than the teeth of your comb. Starting close to the scalp, slide comb up the hair approximately 1½ inches.

2 Slide comb down towards roots. Work up the lengths in this way, gradually forming a pad of backcombing at the scalp.

3 One firmly backcombed mesh of hair.

4 Once the entire head has been backcombed, smooth over lightly with a brush and pull curls into place with the fingers.

5 Should the curl have lost its definition, spray with a fine mist of water or use a tiny amount of mousse on the ends. The picture shows the stunning effect that can be attained simply by using gel and the correct drying technique.

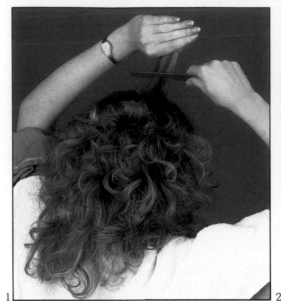

1

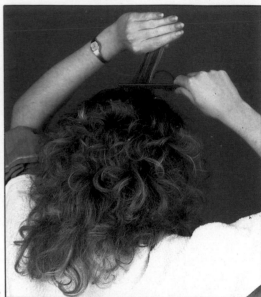

2

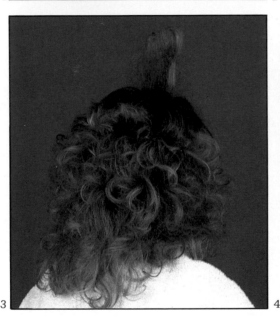

3

4

accordingly. Where once a light cream rinse was sufficient, a more penetrating moisture/protein pack may now be required, especially if your hair is permed or tinted.

Dryness in hair also means a dry scalp, and you will find that your scalp feels a little tighter and is more sensitive, so remember to have a skin test prior to a colour application, and do take care if you do a home perm.

Stress can affect us at any age, but the thirties can be high stress years. Holding down a full-time job, rearing children, running a home, divorce, marriage; all of these put a strain on our bodies and our minds. Help yourself as much as possible, trying to relax, etc., and at the first sign of problems consult your doctor.

Grey hair. Some people have always had the odd stray white hair, but for most of us they seem to creep up unannounced sometime in the thirties – not enough to give a glamorous, distinctive streak but enough to be annoying. White hair is really no different from your other hair, it is just that the melanocytes (colour producing cells) have stopped producing colour, but this does not affect hair growth. Grey hair is in fact white hair, it's only because coloured and white hairs are intermingled that we call it grey. A few stray white hairs can be blended in with a simple semi-permanent colour or highlights, but if you have a high percentage of white hair then you would get more satisfactory coverage from a permanent colour. For more advice on haircolouring see the appropriate chapter.

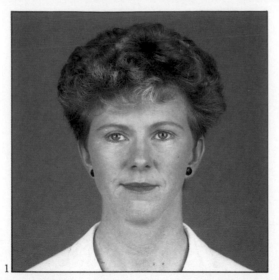

1 Eva is a busy housewife and prefers a short, no-fuss style that stays looking good all day.
2 After blow drying, Eva uses a steam styling brush; this type of styler is very easy to use. Work from the centre to the sides, progressing to the front.

Life begins at forty. How we used to smile at the old adage from the safety of our teenage years. Forty: that seemed so very old. But the tables have turned, and look just how true it has become. Look around at the attractive, successful women in their forties, both housewives and career women.

Unfortunately, if you have abused your hair and skin over the years the problems you started all those years ago may now come home to roost. But fear not, a lot can be done with flattering hairstyles and clever, subtle make-up.

The problems of dry hair, scalp and skin intensify during the forties, so in the same way that you will be lavishing extra attention on your skin, spare a thought for

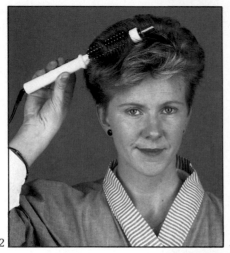

3 Hold the styler in position for a few seconds. If using the brush to boost your style between washes, push the button for instant steam and lasting results.
4 Brush through from the crown working forwards. A vent brush is used, the quills of which are widely spaced, penetrating the hair and producing a more casual result.
5 Smart, easy-to-control style accentuating the neat head shape.
6 The perfect style for a busy housewife or career woman who always needs to look her best.

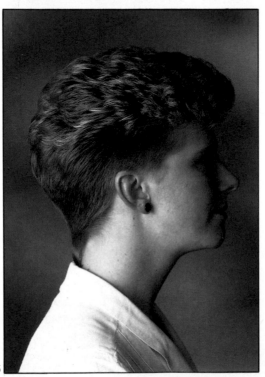

your hair. Use a shampoo especially formulated for dry hair and apply a special moisture protein-enriched treatment once a week or fortnight. You may also find that your scalp is dry and flaky and the temptation will be to reach for a strong, medicated shampoo – don't. It's unlikely to be dandruff; just lack of natural oils. Treat the hair and scalp for dryness and the problem should abate. Seek professional advice before resorting to strong, medicated shampoos.

Hair colour and make-up should be adjusted as you age, particularly if you have gone very white. Never be tempted to tint your hair very dark, even if you were once a natural brunette, it will just look 'dyed'.

One problem you could face is full, lifeless looking hair, even though the style is perfect. Keep a can of spray hair tonic handy, style and spray as normal, and as a final touch spray very lightly with the tonic. The shine is instant and, providing you're not heavy handed, will not reduce your hair to a flat, oily mess.

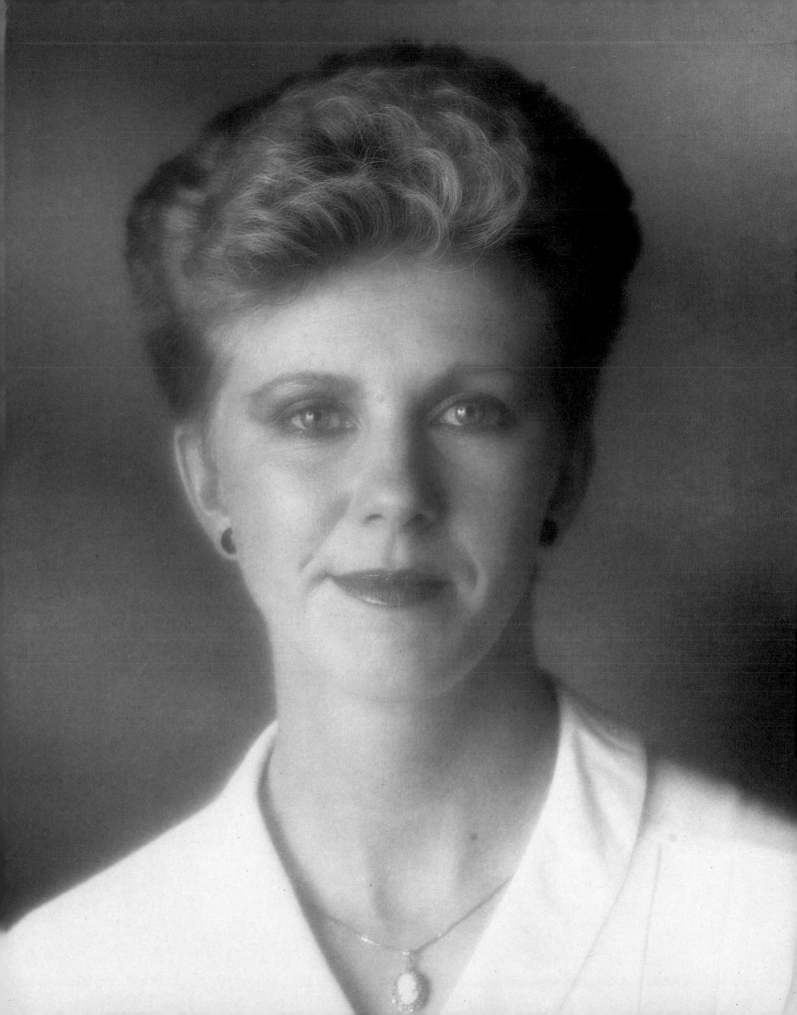

Right: in her early forties, Mirna is fortunate enough to have superb facial bone structure which allows her to wear her hair in a variety of ways.

Below right: this particular design is a slightly longer, softer design than Eva's, on the previous page. After shampooing, hair mousse was applied for added body. The hair was blow dried using a radial bristle brush, following the lines of the cut.

Facing page: a flattering shape which relies on the all-important cut, which is the foundation for any style, no matter what age you are.

Stylewise, keep it soft and easy to manage, and avoid tight, curly perms, they are so aging. Teach yourself to blow-dry and use a hot brush. If you prefer to roller set, then follow some of the guidelines illustrated in this chapter. Light fringes hide forehead lines, and swept back sides emphasize the eyes that may now be slightly deeper set.

Looking through some recent press cuttings I came across a photograph of finalists in a glamorous grandmother competition. How different they looked from the average gran of forty years ago: flattering hairstyles with grey hair skilfully coloured, soft layers dressed into full, bouncy shapes framed youthful faces and there were trim figures that would be the envy of many twenty year olds. Who said gran should sit at home knitting? From the look of these ladies they'll be out dancing the night away alongside their daughters.

Long and Lustrous

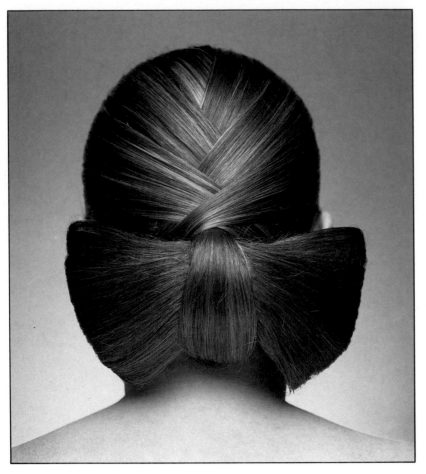

Above: a sleek, sophisticated creation, perfect for that special occasion.
Far right: ornamental combs and pins; the easiest way to enhance the simplest style and cover tell-tale grips and pins.

For many, long hair epitomises the ultimate in femininity, and this attitude applies to both men and women. Perhaps it is a leftover from our cave dwelling heritage, when stone-age man dragged his mate off to his lair by her hair. Does long hair bring out the beast in a man, and is this why so many of us have to grow our hair at least once in the hopes that a virile 'he man' will suddenly appear? Joking apart, once we are old enough to choose our hair's length and style, we all usually go through a long hair phase before finding the style that complements the image we wish to project. For some people long hair will be retained as a curtain to hide behind, or because the men in their lives refuse to let them have it cut. The last reason is one I have heard time and time again over the years. Men seem to disregard the finer points, such as whether long hair suits you, or if it is of the right type and texture to grow long.

For those of you aspiring to long hair here are a few points you should take into consideration.

a Will it suit me – i.e. my facial characteristics?

b Can I cope with it? Shampooing, condition and drying, take more time; long hair must be kept clean and swingy to look good.

c Can I dress my hair into an upswept style myself should the occasion demand?

d Will it fit in with my lifestyle, clothes, job, leisure, etc?

e Am I prepared to have regular haircuts to keep it in peak condition?

f Have I the right type of hair to grow long?

Let's consider each of those points in more detail.

Suitability requires little explanation and depends entirely on the individual. If you already have long hair or are growing it, correct shampooing and conditioning are

The popularity of long hair has waxed and waned according to the whims of fashion. But there are those who, regardless of fashion, will always wear their hair long, and this is just the way it should be, providing of course that long, flowing locks suit you.

Now, more than ever, styles for long hair have greater versatility: from simple braids and chignons to complicated and intricate woven designs. Improved permanent waving products and techniques allow for more scope, so that long hair need not be left just to hang, like Alice in Wonderland's, but can be permed and curled, depending on its texture and condition.

never brush wet hair straight after shampooing, use a comb. If your hair is greasy apply conditioner to middle lengths and ends only, and do not massage into the scalp. Drying: dry naturally whenever possible. If the hair is to be set, then part dry before putting in rollers, protect fragile ends with a small square of tissue. Blowdrying: always remember to direct the air down the hair shaft with the cuticle; never aim the air up from points to roots, if you do you will raise the cuticle, damaging the hair, and the result will be dull, fuzzy, split hair. Never use a very hot dryer close to the hair and always keep the hot air moving.

Naturally, the size roller or brush you use will depend on whether your hair is curly or straight and the degree of curl required: e.g. the smaller the brush or roller the tighter the curl and vice versa. Do bear in mind that the weight of your hair will affect the amount of curl and its holding power. For example, very thick, heavy, straight hair will drop fairly quickly.

Above: hair ornaments come in an amazing variety of shapes and colours. Some of the materials used are pretty unusual as well, ranging from basic plastic to tortoiseshell or leather and crystal as shown here.
Right: the better the equipment, the easier it is to style your hair. Good quality brushes, combs, dryers and rollers are a boon. Don't forget the fun items like bands, bows and even shock waves and colour flashes to brighten your hair.
Far right: plaited strips of suede make simple but effective headgear, especially when coordinated with your outfit.

vitally important. Follow the guidelines described in the previous chapters. Choose a mild shampoo and always use a conditioner. Invest in a wide-toothed comb and a good hairbrush, either bristle or plastic, making sure each quill is well finished and rounded off. When combing, dry or wet, always start at the nape and work from the points (ends of the hair) towards the scalp. Take small sections at a time until all the hair is combed through;

The more classical, upswept styles require a good foundation; the roots must move upwards or back, in the direction of the finished style. Therefore, when you are setting try to imagine the final result and place your rollers accordingly. If you're blow drying, lift the hair with your fingers or a brush and dry thoroughly in an upward direction. This is also a good tip if you intend to wear your hair down and want it to look full and bouncy. Always apply a setting

important date it's wise to experiment a little beforehand. Hopefully, the step by step illustrations shown here will help you. It's a good idea to purchase plenty of hairgrips, fine hairpins, hairspray and some covered elastic bands – you could be surprised at how many you will need!

Padded shapes to help support a full hairstyle come in very handy, particularly if you are not very adept at backcombing. These used to be made from hair combings but nowadays synthetic hair is substituted. Pads come in a variety of shapes and sizes: long sausage shapes, ovals rounds and basic colours such as blonde, brown, black and red. Pinned onto the head they add fullness and eliminate the need for excessive backcombing; the hair is simply

1 Long hair can be a problem on holiday, especially after a day at the beach. Here's a colourful way to pretty up your hair.
2 After shampooing, gather all the wet hair into a high ponytail.

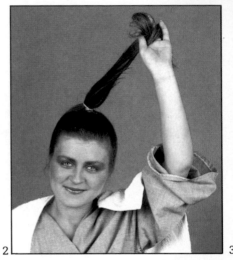

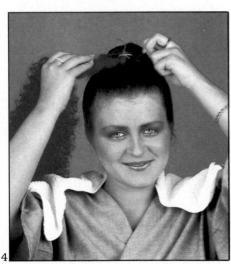

3 Apply gel to the front, sides and nape to keep stray ends in place.
4 Take one very long, brightly coloured switch and pin it firmly in front of the ponytail.
5 Gel ponytail and wrap it around the base of the switch. Secure ends round the bun with hair pins.
6 Cover any visible pins with a ringlet around the base of the bun.
7 A cascade of colour. This is a quick and novel way to brighten up your hair and a definite eye catcher.

lotion of some description prior to drying as this will prevent your hair from going too soft and flyaway.

Dressing your hair into an upswept, classical style will require patience and practice, so if you're preparing for an

smoothed over the padding and discreetly pinned.

Plain, simple hairstyles are the perfect foil for hair ornaments. It's a good idea to begin a collection of hair accessories such as pretty silk flowers, ribbons, slides and ornamental combs. If you're lucky enough to visit the Far East, watch out for some exquisite hair slides, combs and pins, especially the hand-painted, lacquered variety, as they are usually very resonably priced.

Our lifestyles affect everything we do and wear. If your hair only looks good when it's dressed up, perhaps you should consider a shorter style. But, if you're an aspiring ballet dancer, then long hair is a must as it will have to be worn in a sleek, tight chignon most of the time. These days we have less and less time to pamper ourselves, and if your hair encroaches into your leisure and social life then a style reappraisal is necessary. Long hair obviously takes longer to do than short hair and requires that bit extra care, but for day-to-day styling you should be fairly adept at handling it and not have to spend hours in front of the mirror every morning.

Is your hair of the right type and texture to grow long? There is really only one type of hair that I feel is best worn at a shorter length and this is very fine, thin, fragile hair. If you have this problem hair you have probably already found that it is difficult to grow long. Being so weak it tends to break and split very easily, and the additional length puts more strain on the delicate fibres. Very thick, curly hair has its own problems. There is a tendency for this type of hair to be dry and unruly. As it grows it seems to get wider rather than longer and it is not until it passes the shoulders that there is sufficient weight to keep it down and looking long. However, with perseverance and regular treatments long hair can be yours.

Cutting is vitally important even when you're trying to grow your hair. Six-weekly trims remove unsightly split ends which, left untended, will travel up the hair shaft and require far more drastic cutting than a mere quarter of an inch. It's hard to part with your hair when you're trying to grow it, even the minutest snippet, but remember there is no point in having long hair if it looks like a dried-up haystack.

Hot brushes, curling tongs and heated rollers are a great way to boost any hairstyle, but particularly long hair. Heated rollers add body, curl, and root lift; perfect if you want to put your hair up. Hot brushes

and tongs smooth out frizzy hair and create bounce and curl – especially beneficial for those who prefer casual styles. When using any appliance that invloves direct heat being applied to the hair, take care. Bear in mind that your hair may be over six years old at the points and very fragile; protect the ends of your hair with tissue or wind the hair around the rollers or tongs, starting at the roots, so that the ends come into contact with the heat last of all.

Some timely tips: for a really way-out, curly look try setting your hair in rags. Work with small sections of hair on clean, almost dry, hair. The longer you leave them in, the curlier you'll go. If rags don't appeal, invest in a set of special rollers (available from major stores and hairdressers), similar to a long frankfurter, which are very soft and pliable. The hair is twisted and wound around the roller which is then bent over to

1 The following style is great for wavy, layered hair like Ashley's. If your hair is straight, it's a good idea to curl it first.
2 Section the hair from ear to ear over the crown. Divide front into three – top and two sides – part off a small square on the crown and place remaining hair in a ponytail.
3 Smooth square crown section down close to ponytail and grip just above it; use hairspray to control stray ends.
4 Smooth left side back and over to the right side of the ponytail. Grip close to band.
5 Repeat with right side section, gripping close to left side of ponytail.
6 Use an Afro-type comb to fluff out ponytail.

4

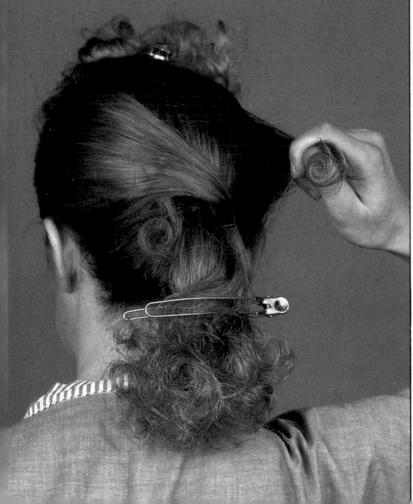

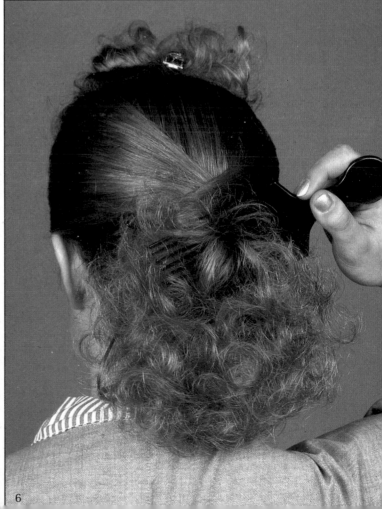

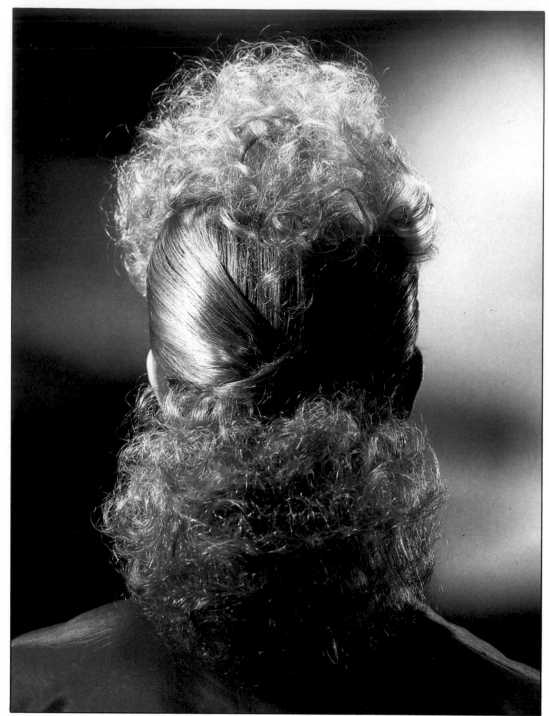

Right: with the ponytail fluffed out, release final top section, fluff out and spray into position as if dressing out shorter hair. This style provides a great contrast in textures ranging from very sleek to a froth of curl.

Facing page: this is an extra, simpler style consisting of just two ponytails, one positioned behind the ear the other at the front, at a diagonal to the first. Backcomb and fluff out both ponytails. Spray and add the finishing touch with two ornamental chop-sticks.

secure it – no pins required. They are great fun to use and less damaging to the hair than small, spiky, plastic rollers.

Permanent waves and colours: long hair should only be permed or coloured by a qualified hairdresser. Never attempt to do it yourself at home. It's worth bearing in mind that if anything goes wrong it can only be cut out, thereby removing many years of growth with one fell swoop of the scissors. If you would like a perm don't expect to get lots of lift and bounce at the roots; this can

only be achieved if the hair is cut shorter on top or in layers, blending from short over the top and crown to very long at the back. So, be prepared to part with some of your hair if your heart is set on a long, full, curly look.

Finally, nothing beats a head of long hair that gleams with health and swings as you walk, and we all envy those with such beautiful hair. Who knows, perhaps the modern version of stone-age man is waiting just around the next corner!

1 Pam has lovely grey hair that she normally blow dries. The soft shape is supported by a body perm.
2 To set, use a styling aid. Pam uses a pearl mousse, which adds a subtle silver tone.
3 Smooth ends over roller and wind down. Secure with plastic pin.
4 Massage mousse through evenly from roots to points.

From facial hair back to hairstyles. Eventually, the menopause will be behind you, the only children you have to look after will be grandchildren, and your life is now your own. Perhaps you still work or are involved in charity work of some kind. It's a great help to get out and become involved with some outside venture that encourages you to mix with people of all ages, and keeps you looking and feeling young and conscious of your appearance. After all, it does not follow that your hairstyle changes to fingerwaves and a hairnet when you turn fifty.

Choose your hairstyle to suit you and your lifestyle. As we age, softer, face-framing styles are more flattering; hard, flat, scraped-back styles only tend to emphasize lines and wrinkles. Try not to let your hair get untidy; wild looks only look sexy on the young. Age must compensate

5 Comb hair in direction to be set. Part a small mesh of hair the same size as roller.
6 Side hair is set in loose pin curls towards back, top rolled to side, crown back.
7 When dry, brush vigorously to blend roller sections. If set is too tight, relax with the blow dryer.

attempt to do it yourself with some sort of home kit; the result could be permanent scarring. Other methods include shaving, a definite NO to this one, and waxing. Waxing is not really suitable for older skins because of facial lines and lack of elasticity, and the majority of manufacturers advise against it. Depilatory creams are cheaper, if rather smelly; ensure that the one you purchase is suitable for the face and follow the directions to the letter. At the first sign of irritation rinse immediately with cold water.

with confidence and elegance; something that is acquired with maturity.

If you want to try a new style, think carefully: is a twice-weekly shampoo and set better for you than a monthly cut which you have to blow dry? This is not because I doubt anyone's ability to blow dry their own hair, but if you suffer from stiffness, rheumatism or arthritis you may find it difficult to hold a blow dryer above shoulder level for a long period of time. If you have the right quality of hair, the ideal style is a perfect cut and easy blow dry, but,

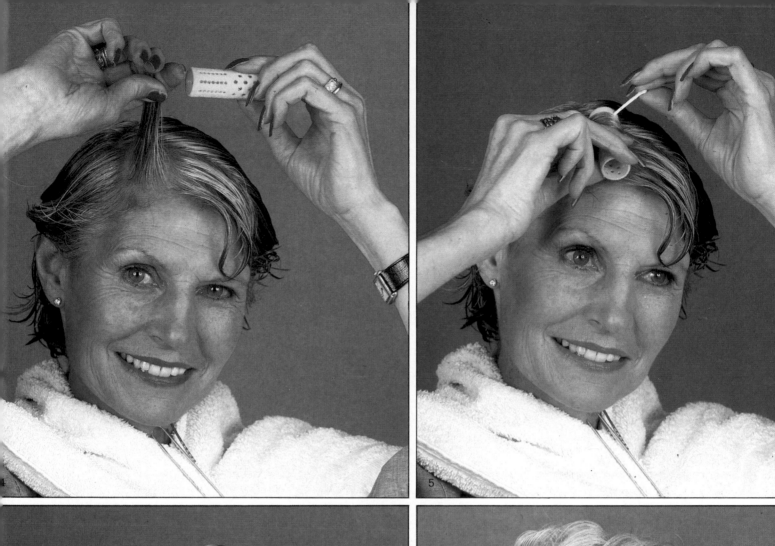

Complete the style with the fingers or a tailcomb. The secret when styling grey hair is not to create hard, rigid lines but to keep the movements soft and flowing. That subtle hint of pearly silver complements Pam's hair and skin tone perfectly.

unfortunately, few of us are blessed with such good-tempered hair.

Hair colours should be subtle. Grey/white hair can look very striking, but beware of yellowness caused by cooking, coal fires and smoking. If you style your own hair then always keep a bottle of silver-coloured setting or blow dry lotion handy; it won't turn your hair blue but it will help to neutralise those yellow tones. If your hair is salt and pepper, try a steel-grey or neutralising ash rinse for a deeper blend of light and dark hair.

Semi-permanent colours help to blend in the grey hair or freshen up hair that looks dull and faded. It's fine to blend in white hair, but do avoid going very dark as it's unlikely to enhance your complexion.

Permanent tints last longer and give better coverage of white hair. Do follow manufacturers' directions if you're tinting at home and, once again, not too dark or exotic. Choose soft browns or blondes with gold or warm tones as these will reflect warmth into your skin, rather than very ash tones which, on a mature person, can make the skin look very pale and ill even though they're fighting fit.

Money can be a problem when a pension has to be stretched to cover all the bills. If you're over sixty, keep an eye on your local salon for special offers, reduced rates, and discounts for senior citizens. Usually, these offers are at the beginning of the week, when salons are quieter, and it can mean a great saving on the normal prices.